SHERLEYS
DOG BOOK

The Complete Book Of Dog Care

Written by a
Veterinary Surgeon

Illustrated by
Gillian Dorsett

SHERLEY'S DIVISION
ASHE LABORATORIES LIMITED

Contents

Thirty-first Edition 1975
© 1975 Ashe Laboratories Limited, Leatherhead, Surrey.

Printed in England by C. B. Printers Ltd.

Chapter 1
CHOOSING AND
KNOWING YOUR DOG

Since the earliest days of man's civilisation the dog has been his friend and companion. Undoubtedly the dog was at first a guard and a hunter, but he very soon moved into the house and became one of the family. In Britain, above all countries, we consider ourselves a nation of animal lovers, so when the time comes for you to choose your new pet, make sure that you do so for the right reasons.

It is now estimated that in Britain only about 50% of pups born each year will be required for adoption. Of the remainder some die of natural causes, some are killed in road accidents, but the total destroyed is now about 900,000 per annum. Of these a large proportion are destroyed by the various Animal Welfare Organisations because they are either lost, unwanted or abandoned by their owners. If we gave more thought to choosing the right pet and then learning how to care for it properly this sad situation could be greatly improved.

The Right Dog For You

If you are really attracted to one particular breed, and interested in showing and breeding, the situation is already decided for you. You will select the dog of your choice and then make whatever changes are necessary in your way of life to suit it. However, for most of us the dog is a pet, a companion and a very important member of the family. It is well worth spending a little time to find the dog which will fit comfortably into your home.

which breed?

The table (page 10) showing various breeds and illustrating their characteristics, will help to guide your choice.

Pedigree Or Cross-breed?

If you buy a pedigree puppy you have a general idea of the shape and size which you can expect in the adult, whereas a mongrel puppy is perhaps more of a gamble. One thing is certain, pedigree or mongrel, you are going to think your dog is the best in the world.

choosing
the puppy

It should be remembered though, that as a result of in-breeding over the years to produce show "characteristics", some of the breeds now possess inherited defects. An example of this is hip dysplasia in some of the larger breeds, retinal atrophy (a form of blindness) in labradors, and a tendency to dislocating joints in poodles, pekes and pugs. It is important to buy your pedigree pup from a reputable breeder. Many poor specimens are sold, especially through dealers, and a certificate of pedigree is not a guarantee of health or soundness. On the other hand the idea that mongrels are hardier, or more resistant to disease is simply an old wives' tale. There is no difference at all in the resistance of pedigrees or cross-breeds, and each requires equal care from their owners. Many mongrels, especially the poodle or small terrier crosses, make charming and intelligent pets, but care should be taken over the larger mixtures such as alsatians and boxers, as they sometimes seem to inherit the aggressive features of each parent.

Dog Or Bitch?

which sex?

People tend to think that a dog is less trouble to keep than a bitch, but this is not necessarily so. A bitch comes in season for three weeks every 6 months and must of course be carefully watched, and kept in. A dog, however, retains its interest in the opposite sex all the year round and if not restrained may start to wander off in search of

The skeleton of the dog.

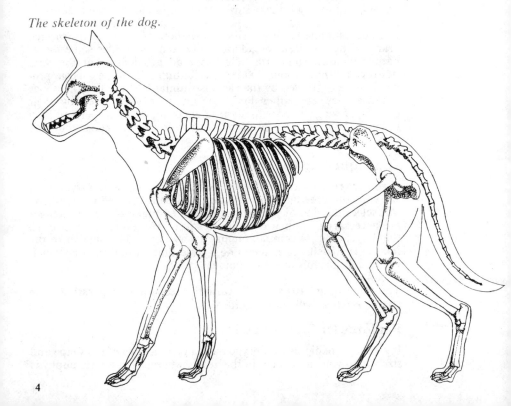

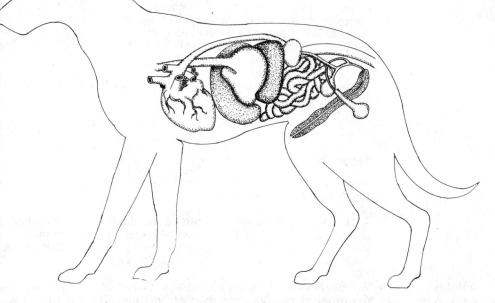

females, becoming a nuisance and a danger on the roads. In addition, bitches often seem to have sweeter dispositions and make better pets, especially where there are children in the house.

Neutering

Both dogs and bitches, like cats, can be neutered and in view of the present population explosion in the dog world it is very well worth considering, not only for your own convenience, but for the social good.

The operation in either case is painless and is carried out under a general anaesthetic. It does not change the animal's character (for good or for bad) and contrary to popular opinion it does not make it fat, provided that it is fed and exercised properly. A bitch which has been sterilised does not come on heat or attract other dogs and is an ideal companion.

If you feel reluctant to consider an operation there are now tablets and sprays available which greatly reduce the nuisance of the heat period.

The Right Size Of Dog

large or small?

However much you may love the thought of a great big dog, do think seriously before buying one. Certainly a big dog is a deterrent to burglars, but a small one with a big bark may do as much good. To

5

be an effective guard, a dog must be properly trained or you may soon find yourself in trouble when he mistakes the postman for an intruder. Obviously if you live in a flat or town house you are going to have problems with an outsize dog, but even in the country a big dog must be exercised, and not allowed to wander and cause danger to livestock. Training is of particular importance with large dogs, as so many, from lack of early training, get beyond their owners' control and have to be destroyed. Big dogs need big fences to keep them in, and very big food bills if they are to be fed properly, so unless your circumstances really justify it, think first, and choose a dog that is just the right size for you.

The table of breeds (page 10) gives some guidance on size and suitability for flat life.

How To Be A Good Owner

Before making the decision about buying a new pup here are some points you should consider:—

1 **Is someone at home for most of the day?** A dog, especially a puppy, should not be left on its own for more than a few hours at a time. If you are out at work from 9-5 don't get a dog, unless you can make really satisfactory arrangements with a neighbour to let it out.

holiday expenses

2 **What about holidays?** It is sad to say that more dogs are destroyed at holiday time than at any other. Unless you have a helpful family to look after your dog, be prepared for the expense of kennels. Because of the increase in cost of labour and food, reputable kennels now have to make a high charge—and don't forget to book well ahead.

3 **Are you prepared for the cost of keeping a dog?** This includes not only the cost of food, and kennels at holiday time, but also the cost of vaccination against the major diseases (this is something which every conscientious owner must have done) and also possible veterinary fees in case of illness. A dog, like a child, can be ill quite suddenly and unexpectedly and there is as yet no National Health Service for dogs, although the various Welfare Organisations such as the RSPCA or PDSA will provide help for those who are in difficult circumstances and unable to afford veterinary fees. There are also some canine health insurance schemes which can be joined to cover major expenses; these however are to take care of eventualities such as emergency surgery.

recognise the costs

plenty of exercise

4 **Exercise.** To keep healthy and happy, dogs need daily exercise, and by this is meant a good run off the lead in a field or park, or a game with a ball, not just a stroll round to the shops on a lead. If you love your dog, be prepared to sacrifice some of your leisure time each day, whatever the weather. If your health or circumstances really do not allow you to provide this type of exercise, consider giving a home to an older dog. Your local RSPCA or Lost Dogs' Home may have just the right one for you.

5   **Family circumstances.** Dogs and children usually love each other
and get on well, but do not make the mistake of buying a young
puppy for a toddler. Young children can be thoughtlessly cruel and
a puppy may be badly pulled about. Worse still a young pup's bones
may be easily broken if a child thinks that it can be treated like the
other cuddly toys. Wait until the children are older and a little more
responsible. They will get much more pleasure out of a dog when
they are old enough to take it for walks.

6   **Grooming.** If you have not much time to spare, choose a dog with
a smooth or wire coat, which needs little attention to keep it tidy.

Long and curly coated dogs look beautiful, but they need daily
grooming to keep them this way. Poodles need regular trimming, as
well as grooming, so unless you are able to do this yourself be
prepared for extra expense.

Buying A Dog

Beware of the impulse buy. It is hard to resist the appeal of a puppy
in a shop window, especially if it looks a little bit sad and wistful,
but these unlucky pups have already had two changes of home and
often a long train journey from their original breeder. Even though
they appear well, they may be in the early stages of infectious disease
and you may find yourself involved not only in trouble, but heartbreak as well. So make sure first that the shop is reputable.

Whenever possible visit the home of the breeder, or the owner of the
bitch. You will be able to ensure that your pup came from a clean
and healthy home, and you may get helpful advice about the kind of
diet and training that your pup has been used to.

Be particularly careful about buying a pup through a newspaper
advertisement, without seeing it first. There is a wise saying 'buyer
beware' and this applies especially to all kinds of livestock. If your
new dog is ill when it arrives, or quite unlike the promises of the
advertisement, you may find it very difficult to get any satisfaction.

Even in the case of a money-back guarantee, it is very little
compensation for the disappointment, especially where there are
children involved. You may decide to get a dog from a Dogs' Home,
or from one of the Welfare Societies and this is well worth considering. You will have the satisfaction of feeling that you are saving
a life and giving some unwanted pet a home. It is as well to
remember though that young dogs that have been straying for sometime may have picked up distemper and that some thoughtless
owners take their dogs to a Dogs' Home because they have become
unmanageable in some way. In the case of a bitch she may turn out
to be in pup and you will find yourself saddled with rather more dogs
that you can manage. Don't just fall for the first dog that you see,
(and it can be very hard not to), but talk to the officials at the Home
and try to find out a little of the background.

Choosing A Healthy Pup

It is often difficult for a beginner to distinguish a healthy pup from a
poor one—to them one attractive little bundle of fur looks very like

another—but really there is all the difference in the world. A healthy pup should be plump, but not have a swollen or blown-up stomach. Its skin should feel loose and pick up easily, instead of seeming to stick to the bones, because there is a healthy layer of fat under the skin. The coat should shine (except in the case of wirehaired varieties) and of course should be free from fleas or lice. The eyes should be bright and free from any sign of discharge. In addition it is wise to choose a pup which is lively and readily comes to greet people. A timid or withdrawn type of pup may have a problem personality and be difficult to train. Finally, don't be surprised if a conscientious dog breeder wants to ask a lot of questions to find out if you are going to be a suitable person to own one of his pups.

Your Dog And The Law

licences

All dogs must have a licence from the age of 6 months and must wear a collar, with a name tag showing your address. This is obviously of the greatest importance, as if your pup should stray, or be involved in an accident, it can then be traced. It has been suggested that all dogs should be tattooed with an identity number; this would probably do much to reduce the present huge number of strays, but unfortunately the idea does not work on black dogs!

road safety

In many roads dogs are not allowed unless on a lead. This is mainly to prevent road accidents, but with the ever increasing traffic problem, no conscientious owner should allow a pet to wander in the streets, for its own sake.

If you live in a country district take special care to see that your dog does not wander away on its own. Dogs cause terrible damage each year to sheep and lambs, and a dog may be shot by a farmer if it is seen in suspicious circumstances.

pollution

Pollution is now a great problem in the world. Take care that your dog is trained to the gutter and never fouls the footpath. The penalty in some districts may be as much as £20 and more than that, it is the duty of all dog lovers to see that their pets do not cause annoyance to the rest of the world.

Points Of The Dog

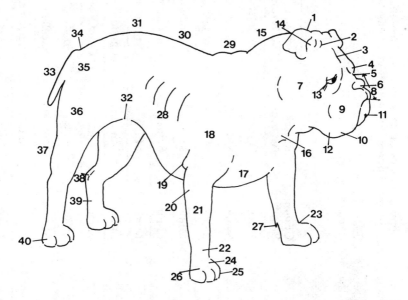

TECHNICAL TERMS

(1) Apex of Skull	(21) Forearm
(2) Skull	(22) Knee
(3) Groove	(23) Pastern
(4) Temples or Frontal Bones	(24) Fore-feet
(5) Stop	(25) Toes
(6) Nose	(26) Knuckles
(7) Cheek	(27) Dew-claw
(8) Layback	(28) Ribs
(9) Cushion	(29) Wither
(10) Chop or Flews	(30) Back
(11) Underjaw	(31) Loin
(12) Corner of the Jaw	(32) Belly
(13) Corner of the Eye	(33) Tail
(14) Set of Ear	(34) Set of Tail or Stern
(15) Neck	(35) Hip Joint
(16) Dewlap	(36) Thigh
(17) Brisket	(37) Stifle
(18) Shoulder	(38) Hock
(19) Elbow	(39) Pastern
(20) Calf	(40) Hind-foot

Table Of Different Breeds And Suitablity

This table lists some (but not all) of the most popular breeds of dogs and indicates the adult size (L = large, M = medium and S = small), suitability for children, amount of grooming and exercise required and suitability for flat life.
Remember that this is for guidance only; some breeds will have small and large varieties in the breed (i.e. poodles, dachshunds, etc.) and that individual temperament and training will reflect in the characters of all dogs.

Breed	Size	Suitability to Children	Grooming Required	Exercise Needed	Suitability to Flat Living
Afghan	L	Excellent	Much	Some	Can tolerate
Airedale	L	Good	Some	Much	Can tolerate
Alsatian	L	Good	Some	Much	Can tolerate
Basset	M	Excellent	Minimal	Minimal	Can tolerate
Beagle	S	Good	Minimal	Some	Can tolerate
Boxer	L	Good	Minimal	Much	Can tolerate
Bulldog	M	Excellent	Minimal	Minimal	Can tolerate
Cairn	S	Good	Some	Some	Good
Cavalier King Charles Spaniel	S	Good	Some	Some	Good
Chihuahua	S	Not recommended	Minimal	Minimal	Excellent
Chow Chow	M	Not recommended	Much	Some	Can tolerate
Cocker Spaniel	M	Excellent	Much	Some	Good
Collie	L	Excellent	Some	Some	Poor
Dachshund	S	Good	Minimal	Minimal	Excellent

Breed	Size				
Dalmatian	L	Excellent	Minimal	Some	Can tolerate
Dobermann	L	Not recommended	Minimal	Much	Can tolerate
English Springer Spaniel	M	Excellent	Much	Much	Can tolerate
Fox Terrier	S	Excellent	Minimal	Some	Good
Great Dane	L	Excellent	Some	Some	Can tolerate
Irish Setter	M	Good	Some	Much	Can tolerate
Old English Sheepdog	L	Excellent	Much	Much	Poor
Pekinese	S	Not recommended	Much	Minimal	Excellent
Pembroke Corgi	S	Good	Minimal	Some	Good
Poodle	S	Good	Much	Some	Excellent
Pug	S	Good	Minimal	Minimal	Excellent
Retriever	L	Excellent	Some	Much	Can tolerate
Labrador Retriever	L	Excellent	Some	Much	Can tolerate
Scottish Terrier	S	Not recommended	Some	Some	Good
Shetland Sheepdog	M	Excellent	Much	Some	Good
Shih Tzu	S	Good	Much	Minimal	Excellent
Staffordshire Bull Terrier	M	Good	Minimal	Some	Good
West Highland White	S	Good	Much	Minimal	Excellent
Whippet	M	Good	Minimal	Much	Can tolerate
Yorkshire Terrier	S	Good	Much	Minimal	Excellent

Chapter 2
BREEDING AND REARING DOGS

Rearing a litter of puppies can be a delightful and rewarding experience, but it should not be undertaken without a certain amount of serious thought. Even assuming that you love dogs, and will consider the hard work involved as no disadvantage, it is sadly true that there are already far more dogs in the world than there are kind and welcoming homes to take them. In other words, dogs too are suffering from a population explosion.

family planning too!

If you own a bitch you may want to let her have a litter, so that you have a home grown pup to add to your family. That is fine, but do make sure especially in the case of cross-breeds, that you can find good homes for the other pups. If not, harden your heart and ask your veterinary surgeon or local Animal Welfare Clinic to destroy them painlessly. It is very hard to make this decision over a little furry bundle one day old, but it is heart-breaking with a pup 8 or 10 weeks old. To take your surplus pups to a Dogs' Home is simply to shirk your responsibilities. You will have no idea of where they may end up, and too many people take on a pup on impulse, only to discard it when it becomes a nuisance.

should you breed your dog?

There is a popular idea that it does a dog or bitch good to be mated, but there is very little evidence to support this. The dog which tends to be over-sexed will not be improved by being used once or twice at stud. Some bitches make excellent mothers and obviously enjoy maternity, but for others it can be a difficult or a painful experience. There is no evidence that having a litter of pups has a beneficial effect on either the health or the temperament of a bitch, and one would very much doubt if the ordinary, happy family pet ever feels that she is unlucky to have been deprived of the chance to rear a litter. By all means rear a litter of pups if you really want them, but not just because you feel you should.

Breeding Pedigree Pups

Do not go into dog breeding in the expectation of making money. The idea of selling a large litter at a high price may sound inviting, but the cost of rearing puppies properly can be considerable, and there are many pitfalls on the way. Your bitch may have only one or two pups, or may lie on a beautiful litter and kill them, or she may need a caesarean operation which will leave you well out of pocket.

choosing the breed

Try to choose a popular breed which will sell well. One of the small but sturdy varieties is wisest for the beginner, such as corgis, miniature poodles, cairns or west highlands. The tiny or toy breeds like chihuahuas, pekes, or toy poodles can be difficult to whelp and delicate to rear.

Labradors and dalmatians are popular and have large litters, but if several bitches whelp at about the same time the market in your district may become rather flooded and eight or nine unsaleable pups can eat a great deal of food. If you have good pups it is worth advertising in one of the dog papers as well as in your local press.

buying your dogs

Many people, when planning to start breeding dogs, go out and buy a bitch and a dog. While this sounds reasonable it is not really a practical idea. Your bitch will come in season twice each year and it is obviously not kind or sensible to breed from her at every season. You will then have to board one of the dogs out, or suffer all the inconvenience of trying to keep them apart. It is much wiser to buy two bitches and then when the time comes, select a suitable stud dog, and preferably one that is known to be producing good litters with the characteristics you hope to see in your pups. It is even less of a gamble to consider buying an adult bitch, which has already had one successful litter, but unfortunately these are the very bitches which breeders want to keep.

The Stud Dog

The owner of a stud dog will charge a fee for the mating, and the amount may vary greatly with the pedigree and the show reputation of the dog. Sometimes an arrangement may be reached whereby the owner of the stud dog will agree to take the pup which is 'the pick of the litter' instead of a payment at the time of mating. Usually, if the mating is unsuccessful and there are no puppies the owner of the stud dog may allow you to bring your bitch back at the next season without charge, but this is something that the two parties concerned must decide for themselves, and it is best that it should be in writing.

fees and terms

Keeping A Stud Dog

If you are interested in showing, and if your dog is proving successful and winning prizes you may make a profitable side line out of using him at stud, that is to say, mating him to suitable bitches. Obviously the fee you charge will depend on the quality of your dog. A stud dog should be healthy and fit and should receive a good balanced diet, but there is no need to give him any particularly elaborate diet. It is not desirable that he should be overweight.

13

Monorchids Or Cryptorchids

These are dogs in which one, or both testicles have been retained in the abdomen. They are able to breed, but should not be used at stud, as they may pass on the fault to their pups.

Breeding Terms

Sometimes if the prospective buyer is unable to afford to pay for a bitch at the time, a breeder may suggest selling it on 'breeding terms'. This means that the breeder will be entitled to half of one or more litters. While this may sound tempting it is better to stop and think. It may work out well, but your dog will not be truly your own for a long time and it can well lead to difficulties and disagreements.

Recognition Of Heat

in season

In most cases the first sign of heat (or season or oestrus) is that your bitch becomes very interesting to any male dog that you may happen to meet. You will probably notice that there is a marked swelling of the vulva (the external genital opening) and this becomes noticeable up to the 12th-14th day, after onset of heat. There is usually a clear or whitish discharge which later becomes blood-stained. It may sometimes happen that the first indication you get is when you notice a few spots of blood on the floor.

There is a considerable difference in the amount of evidence of heat which different bitches show. In some it may pass almost unnoticed (so the owner must take special care), while in others there is considerable bleeding. A season usually lasts about 21 days, but care should be taken after this time, if dogs still seem to be interested.

Management Of The Bitch In Season

Many people feel apprehensive about owning a bitch for the first time, because of the supposed problems when they come into season. This is a pity as today there are many quite efficient ways of dealing with the situation, and over all bitches tend to have sweeter dispositions and make better pets.

Surgical Sterilisation— Or Spaying

This is the most effective and permanent method, and is advisable in any case where you have decided quite definitely that you do not want pups in the future. The operation is usually carried out before the first season (although it may be done later).

spaying

The operation requires a general anaesthetic and your bitch will need a little extra care and nursing for a period of about a week. After the operation, the bitch will be free from all the symptoms of heat, and also free from the 'false pregnancy' symptoms which sometimes follow. There are no adverse effects on the health, or the temperament, of the bitch (indeed the guide dogs for the blind are always spayed). There may be a slightly increased tendency to put on weight, but this can be controlled by sensible feeding and exercise.

Hormonal Control

This temporary method, which must be carried out under the supervision of a veterinary surgeon, can be very successful in preventing or postponing the season, though it may not always prevent the occurrence of false pregnancy. It is useful for people who may want to breed from their bitch later, or for postponing a season which might interfere with a show or a holiday.

Deodorant Tablets Or Sprays

These do not prevent the season, but minimise the inconvenience. Amplex Veterinary Tablets help to remove the odour of the bitch which attracts dogs. Sherley's No-fol aerosol masks it by an external repellent effect. While these are a great help in preventing followers from gathering on your doorstep it should be remembered that the

bitch could still be mated if she got out by accident. It is wiser not to leave her unwatched even in a garden or yard that you consider safe. Dogs can show amazing ingenuity in getting in, and a normally home-loving bitch may, when she is in season, try to get out in search of a mate.

With a small dog it is always worth carrying her a little way away from the house before exercising her, so that if any dog should by chance pick up the scent he will not be led to your front door.

Misalliance Or Mis-mating

If in spite of all your care your bitch should be mated accidentally, it is possible to prevent conception by the injection of a hormone preparation, provided that it is given within 48 hours. It is best to consult your veterinary surgeon or local Animal Welfare Clinic as soon as possible. It is sometimes said that a pedigree bitch that has been mis-mated is 'spoiled' for further breeding. This is of course quite untrue. If she is mated to a pedigree dog at the next season she will produce pedigree pups.

False Pregnancy

In the period usually between 6-8 weeks after a season many bitches will show some symptoms of the condition known as 'false pregnancy', although they have not been mated. These may vary from very slight swelling of the milk glands, with the secretion of a little watery fluid, to marked abdominal swelling and the production of large quantities of milk. The psychological symptoms may be even more marked. The bitch becomes restless and may cry a lot. She will usually scratch up her bedding to make a nest for the phantom pups, and in some cases carry a doll or a woolly toy about, and growl in a very possessive way if anyone approaches.

This curious behaviour is really the normal reaction of a bitch to the action of its hormones. If the symptoms are only slight, there is no need to worry. It is a good idea to take the sufferer out and take her mind off the situation, rather than leaving her to brood in her basket. There are tablets such as Sherley's Milk Suppression Tablets which may be given to relieve the distress. If the symptoms are very pronounced it is best to consult a veterinary surgeon.

Mating Your Bitch

age to
mate

Although a bitch may start to come into season from soon after 6 months, it is not advisable to mate her until she is about 18 months old. Up to a year old she is still growing and the strain of producing a litter of pups at this time might well retard her development. Ideally she should be in good bodily condition, but not overweight. It is probably wiser not to mate your bitch for the first time any later than at 5 years old, although there are cases such as the 11 year old terrier that surprised her owner with a healthy first litter. She was obviously the exception to the rule.

The Right Time

Ten days from the commencement of the season is usually considered to be the right time to mate a bitch, but as it is quite difficult for an inexperienced person to be sure which was the first day, probably it is safer to say somewhere between the 8th and 15th days. If you feel doubtful, consult the owner of the stud dog. Very often a breeder will agree to board your bitch for a day or two, to ensure a satisfactory mating. Incidentally, it really is cheaper in the long run to use an approved stud dog, rather than the dog next door.

choosing a
stud dog

Pet dogs are sometimes reluctant or difficult to mate, and if you have misjudged the correct day you may have missed your chance of having a litter of puppies for another 6 months. It is only fair to say though that if your bitch gets out on her own she will probably mate quite successfully with the most unsuitable dog that she meets. During mating, after the dog has mounted the bitch, the two may remain 'tied' for a period of 15 minutes or longer. This is quite usual, but equally there may be a satisfactory mating without a tie.

Pregnancy

Pregnancy in the bitch lasts 63 days, but there may be a variation of several days in either direction. The whelping table will enable you to see the approximate date at which the pups are due. Pups that are

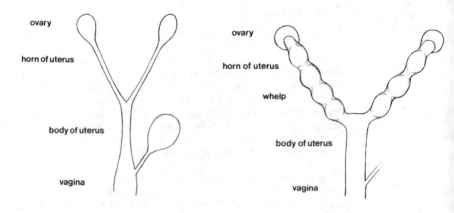

Bitch's uterus before mating.

Bitch's uterus with whelps at 3 weeks.

16

WHELPING TABLE

Served January	Due to Whelp March	Served February	Due to Whelp April	Served March	Due to Whelp May	Served April	Due to Whelp June	Served May	Due to Whelp July	Served June	Due to Whelp August	Served July	Due to Whelp September	Served August	Due to Whelp October	Served September	Due to Whelp November	Served October	Due to Whelp December	Served November	Due to Whelp January	Served December	Due to Whelp February
1	5	1	5	1	3	1	3	1	3	1	3	1	2	1	3	1	3	1	3	1	3	1	2
2	6	2	6	2	4	2	4	2	4	2	4	2	3	2	4	2	4	2	4	2	4	2	3
3	7	3	7	3	5	3	5	3	5	3	5	3	4	3	5	3	5	3	5	3	5	3	4
4	8	4	8	4	6	4	6	4	6	4	6	4	5	4	6	4	6	4	6	4	6	4	5
5	9	5	9	5	7	5	7	5	7	5	7	5	6	5	7	5	7	5	7	5	7	5	6
6	10	6	10	6	8	6	8	6	8	6	8	6	7	6	8	6	8	6	8	6	8	6	7
7	11	7	11	7	9	7	9	7	9	7	9	7	8	7	9	7	9	7	9	7	9	7	8
8	12	8	12	8	10	8	10	8	10	8	10	8	9	8	10	8	10	8	10	8	10	8	9
9	13	9	13	9	11	9	11	9	11	9	11	9	10	9	11	9	11	9	11	9	11	9	10
10	14	10	14	10	12	10	12	10	12	10	12	10	11	10	12	10	12	10	12	10	12	10	11
11	15	11	15	11	13	11	13	11	13	11	13	11	12	11	13	11	13	11	13	11	13	11	12
12	16	12	16	12	14	12	14	12	14	12	14	12	13	12	14	12	14	12	14	12	14	12	13
13	17	13	17	13	15	13	15	13	15	13	15	13	14	13	15	13	15	13	15	13	15	13	14
14	18	14	18	14	16	14	16	14	16	14	16	14	15	14	16	14	16	14	16	14	16	14	15
15	19	15	19	15	17	15	17	15	17	15	17	15	16	15	17	15	17	15	17	15	17	15	16
16	20	16	20	16	18	16	18	16	18	16	18	16	17	16	18	16	18	16	18	16	18	16	17
17	21	17	21	17	19	17	19	17	19	17	19	17	18	17	19	17	19	17	19	17	19	17	18
18	22	18	22	18	20	18	20	18	20	18	20	18	19	18	20	18	20	18	20	18	20	18	19
19	23	19	23	19	21	19	21	19	21	19	21	19	20	19	21	19	21	19	21	19	21	19	20
20	24	20	24	20	22	20	22	20	22	20	22	20	21	20	22	20	22	20	22	20	22	20	21
21	25	21	25	21	23	21	23	21	23	21	23	21	22	21	23	21	23	21	23	21	23	21	22
22	26	22	26	22	24	22	24	22	24	22	24	22	23	22	24	22	24	22	24	22	24	22	23
23	27	23	27	23	25	23	25	23	25	23	25	23	24	23	25	23	25	23	25	23	25	23	24
24	28	24	28	24	26	24	26	24	26	24	26	24	25	24	26	24	26	24	26	24	26	24	25
25	29	25	29	25	27	25	27	25	27	25	27	25	26	25	27	25	27	25	27	25	27	25	26
26	30	26	30	26	28	26	28	26	28	26	28	26	27	26	28	26	28	26	28	26	28	26	27
27	31	27	1 (May)	27	29	27	29	27	29	27	29	27	28	27	29	27	29	27	29	27	29	27	28
28	1 (Apr.)	28	2	28	30	28	30	28	30	28	30	28	29	28	30	28	30	28	30	28	30	28	1 (Mar.)
29	2	29	3	29	31	29	1 (July)	29	31	29	31	29	30	29	31	29	1 (Dec.)	29	31	29	31	29	2
30	3			30	1 (June)	30	2	30	1 (Aug.)	30	1 (Sep.)	30	1 (Oct.)	30	1 (Nov.)	30	2	30	1 (Jan.)	30	1 (Feb.)	30	3
31	4			31	2			31	2			31	2	31	2			31	2			31	4

born more than one week premature have a greatly reduced chance of survival. They are weak, sometimes short of hair, and find it difficult to feed. Overdue pups are better equipped for life, but their increased size may make for difficulties at birth.

recognition of pregnancy

In an overweight bitch, or one that is really muscular, pregnancy may be very difficult to detect. At 3 weeks after mating, a veterinary surgeon may be able to detect the presence of puppies in the abdomen, which at this time feel rather like golf balls. After this time the pups start to grow, and become surrounded by protective fluid, and they may be much less easy to detect. At 6-7 weeks the enlargement of the abdomen becomes apparent and increases rapidly up to full term at 9 weeks.

From about 6-7 weeks also the mammary or milk glands begin to swell, and there may often be milk present, or overflowing in the last week.

The presence of pups may be detected in the last weeks of pregnancy (when their bones have become sufficiently developed) by the use of X-rays, but this is as a rule only done if there is some doubt as to whether the bitch is actually in whelp, or is very overdue.

Preparing For The Pups

It is important to decide in good time just where your bitch is going to have her pups. At this time, like people, they can become rather temperamental and she may be planning to have them on your eiderdown. Choose a quiet corner of the house, where she will not be disturbed, especially if there are children in the house, and get her used to sleeping there in the last week of pregnancy.

the bed and bedding

A suitable bed is a box, with sides of about 8″ high to prevent the pups rolling out. A railing or shelf a few inches away from each inside wall is a help to prevent the pups from being crushed when the mother turns round carelessly in the first few days. The box should

Whelping box showing drop-front and protective shelf.

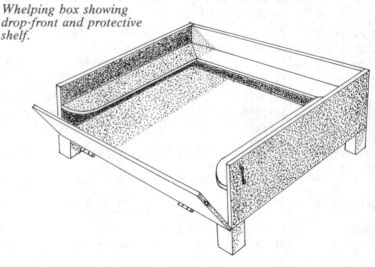

be in a situation free from draughts, as changes in temperature can be very harmful to new-born pups. A thick layer of clean newspaper is the ideal bedding material during whelping. A layer or two can be removed at a time, as it becomes soiled, without disturbing the bitch too much.

Diet During Pregnancy

The in-whelp bitch should be fit, but not fat, so take care to increase the amount of food to be given rather cautiously, but be sure it is of high nutritional value.

In the first 3 weeks the growth of the pups is comparatively slow (indeed at this stage you may not be certain that your bitch is in pup), so it is wise to keep to her normal balanced diet.

From 4-9 weeks the growth of the pups is considerable, and the bitch will require a high food intake, especially of protein, if she is not to lose condition. Protein—that is to say, meat, fish, eggs and offal, should form at least 50% of the diet at this time, the remaining proportion being cereals and biscuit. Fresh liver should be given if possible from time to time, because of its high vitamin B content.

Vegetables may be included in the diet, both for their nutritional value and laxative effect. Sherley's Lactol is of great value at this time for its vitamin A and D content. Sherley's Cod Liver Oil Capsules are also a rich, natural source of vitamins A and D.

vitamin and mineral supplements

A dog receiving the suggested diet will probably be getting an adequate supply of vitamins, but for the bitch which is in poor condition, or one that is reluctant to take one of the essential foods a vitamin supplement is wise, such as Sherley-Vites Condition Tablets.

The normal diet of the dog does not supply adequate amounts of minerals for the pregnant bitch, to build strong bones in the pups, so a mineral supplement should be added to the diet daily. Sherley-Vites and Sherley's Lintox Tonic are both rich in minerals. You will probably find that your bitch becomes extremely hungry as the pregnancy progresses so it is best to divide the meal and feed three time daily, giving perhaps beaten egg, Lactol and cereals for one meal, and the meat mixture at the other two. Where there is a large number of pups present the bitch may become less willing to eat in the later stages of pregnancy because of the abdominal discomfort, so it is wise to give small but frequent meals.

laxatives

It is as well to see that the bitch is free from constipation in the later stages of pregnancy and a mild laxative may be given (but not castor oil). Sherley's Lik-A-Med Laxative is gentle in action and easy to administer. Normal exercise should be continued through

exercise

pregnancy, until the bitch becomes too heavy to consider the daily walk a pleasure. Boisterous games, or running for a ball should be discouraged.

If you normally bath your dog fairly frequently, it is safe to continue in pregnancy, but if there is likely to be any struggling it is better to use a dry cleaning powder such as Sherley's Grooming Powder or

Sherley's Dry Bath, a dry, spirit shampoo that can be rubbed through the coat. For long-haired dogs such as pekes or poodles it will be found very helpful if the hair is trimmed from under the tail, and round the milk glands, to avoid soiling.

Treatment For Worms

It is important to treat your bitch for roundworms immediately before and after whelping (see Chapter 5 on Internal Parasites).

In the adult dog few roundworms are found in the gut, but their larvae remain as cysts in the muscles. Under the influence of the hormones secreted by the bitch during pregnancy these cysts develop into adult worms. The eggs are shed from the bowel, and the bitch while cleaning herself and her puppies soon becomes re-infected, as do the pups themselves. This is the reason why pups may show a severe worm infestation, when the mother was apparently free, or when she was known to have been treated early in pregnancy.

Before the actual birth commences, it is a good idea to check that you have the following things in the house:

1. Soap, disinfectant, and a small hand basin—hygiene is of first importance when handling the mother or pups.
2. Cotton wool for cleaning the pups' noses and mouths.
3. Several old small towels for drying the pups if necessary.
4. A pair of scissors, sterilised by boiling.
5. Some thick silk or cotton (boiled) to tie off the umbilical cords if necessary.
6. A cardboard box, containing a blanket, and a well wrapped hot water bottle, where the first pups may be placed if the bitch becomes upset and restless as other pups arrive.
7. Plenty of clean newspaper.

Behaviour At Whelping Time

In some instances the first stage of labour may be missed altogether, and you may come down to find that a litter of pups has arrived with very little warning. However, if you suspect that the pups are on the way it is wise to stay up, or to come down from time to time to check that all is well. It is a good idea to let your veterinary surgeon know in advance the date of the expected whelping, in case you need to call for his aid at some unsuitable hour.

More often the first stage lasts for 24 hours, or even longer in the maiden bitch. There is usually marked restlessness, panting and sometimes crying, and the bitch will scratch up her bedding a great deal, imitating the behaviour of the primitive dog making a nest for its young. She will generally refuse food, and the temperature if checked will be found to have fallen from the normal of 101.5°F to 98°F. There is usually a rather clear, or mucous-like, discharge from the vulva, and the bitch will probably start to lick and clean herself a great deal.

Normally after the period of restlessness of the first stage of labour the bitch will go into the second stage of labour, in which contractions take place, as the bitch strains to expel the puppy. If these contractions do not follow after a reasonable time, or if the bitch appears to settle down again, it is wise to call a veterinary surgeon. It may be due to a condition known as primary uterine inertia, and an injection may be needed to accelerate the birth processes.

At this time there will be more discharge and sometimes the appearance of the water bag, a membrane filled with fluid at the vulva. This is the protective sac in which the puppy has developed inside the mother. If the bitch continues to strain vigorously for longer than an hour without managing to expel the pup, it is wise to call for professional help, as there may be some abnormality. With a first litter the arrival of the first pup may cause considerable distress, but the later births may be comparatively easy.

Normal Birth

In the canine species the young are born in almost equal numbers, head first (which is usually considered as normal presentation) and hind feet first (or breech). The pup may be born still in its protective sac, but more commonly the sac will rupture, liberating a certain amount of clear fluid and the pup will be seen to be attached to its mother by the umbilical cord. This cord is attached to the placenta or afterbirth and this may be expelled with the pup (the third stage of labour).

the new-born pup

The mother will then start to lick vigorously at the puppy, thus stimulating his breathing, and you will hear him gasp, or perhaps give his first indignant cry at her rough treatment. The mother will then as a rule bite at the umbilical cord to sever it, (there is rarely much bleeding) and she will then eat the afterbirth. This may look

The normal position of the pup at birth.

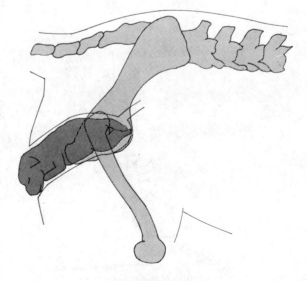

revolting, but dogs have always done so, and there is a theory that there may be hormones in the membranes which are of value to the bitch. The placenta and foetal membranes of the bitch are normally a dark green in colour, and the bitch will tend to have a greenish or blood-stained discharge for some days after the birth of the pups. If the pup is strong and healthy he will almost at once make his way to the milk glands and start feeding. If the birth is proceeding normally, it is best to leave the bitch undisturbed as far as possible, but the owner should stay near at hand in case of difficulties. A puppy may easily be lost for lack of a little assistance at the right moment.

With a first litter, the bitch may at first appear rather mystified, or even frightened of the first pup. It is important then to break immediately the sac, if the pup is still in it, either with the fingers or with sterilised scissors, open the mouth to start the pup breathing and rub it fairly vigorously with a soft, dry towel.

cutting the cord

If the pup is still attached to the placenta (or the mother) by its umbilical cord this must be cut. First tie off the cord firmly about 2″ away from the pup, taking care not to pull at the stomach wall, then cut through on the side away from the knot using the sterilised scissors. As soon as possible put the pup back with its mother, talking to her soothingly until she accepts it.

After the arrival of the first pup the bitch may feel very tired and settle down for a sleep. Usually after a period varying from 20 minutes to an hour or more the contractions will start again, and the rest of the pups will be born at various intervals. If longer than three hours elapses without any straining it is best to consult a veterinary surgeon. Particularly in older dogs the muscle of the uterus (womb) becomes fatigued, and again an injection may be necessary. This is called secondary uterine inertia.

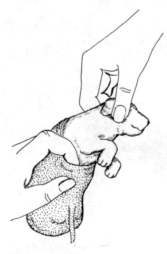

Removing the pup from its protective sac.

Tying and cutting the umbilical cord.

Sometimes the afterbirth is not expelled at the same time as the puppy, but may be shed with or after the next pup. It is important to check that one afterbirth has arrived with each puppy, as if one is retained it can lead to serious illness in the bitch.

If the bitch does not at once take to her pups, or if she becomes restless and inclined to tread on them, when contractions start again, they should be placed in a box in a warm spot, with a well protected hot water bottle. They will soon stop crying and snuggle up to the heat.

Revival Of Pups

Even if a puppy at birth looks blue, cold and dead, it may still be capable of revival. At once place it in a warm spot (at about 80°F), open its mouth and pull the tongue out gently and blow into the mouth, in the manner of mouth to mouth resuscitation. Sometimes one spot of brandy on the tongue will cause it to gasp and start breathing. Continue rubbing all over gently with a pad of cotton wool, or soft towel. If any breathing is seen it is well worth perservering. Pups have been known to recover even after an hour of apparent death.

Normal And Abnormal Presentations

If the puppy is arriving in either of the two normal presentations or positions (that is head, or breech), but the bitch is having difficulty in expelling it completely, the owner may attempt to help. Grip the pup carefully with a clean dry towel, rotate it slightly, from side to side and then as the bitch strains, pull steadily with a downward action.

Dystokia is the name applied to difficult or abnormal birth. In simple cases it may be possible for an owner to give assistance, but an unqualified person should never attempt an internal manipulation and the use of whelping forceps in inexperienced hands can be very dangerous indeed.

If after the bitch has strained for some time only one foot appears at the vulva it suggests that the pup is in an abnormal or transverse position, and the owner should not on any account attempt to remove the puppy. Get in touch with a veterinary surgeon at once, as any delay may risk the life not only of the pups, but of the mother as well. In an emergency the only helpful action is to attempt to push the pup back beyond the neck of the womb, in the hope that the puppy may turn itself into a more satisfactory position.

Care Of The Bitch After Whelping

It may be difficult for an owner to be certain whether or not a bitch has finished whelping. As a rule, after getting rid of the last pup (and afterbirth) she will stop panting and shivering, clean up herself and her pups, and settle down contentedly to feed her family. If she can be persuaded to go out to relieve herself at this point, it will give you the opportunity to remove the soiled bedding, and to check that the pups are sound and healthy.

If you are uncertain whether or not your bitch has finished whelping, it is always best to consult a veterinary surgeon. It has been known for a bitch to produce a live pup after an interval of 24 hours, but if a dead puppy is retained the bitch will soon become seriously ill.

discharges There will normally be a blood-stained discharge for at least a week after the arrival of the pups, and this will gradually become clear, and dry up altogether. A persistent, or foul smelling discharge is a danger signal, and may indicate the presence of a dead pup, or a retained afterbirth. Get advice at once.

Remember that puppies are normally born with their eyes closed, and do not open them until about the 10th-14th day.

abnormal puppies Occasionally deformed pups are born with abnormalities varying from cleft palate, or the absence of a limb, to the complete absence of the stomach wall. These pups should be removed without the bitch seeing if possible, and painlessly destroyed.

Trouble Affecting The Milk Glands

An excess of milk may cause the bitch to become uncomfortable and restless, and she may refuse to let the pups feed. This can be relieved by squeezing the teat to draw off a little of the milk and reduce the pressure.

The sharp claws of the pups may sometimes make painful scratches on the teats, and in this case it helps to trim the points of the claws with scissors.

mastitis A very hard red or swollen teat may indicate mastitis, or infection, in the milk gland. It is important to get veterinary help as soon as possible as the contaminated milk can cause the death of the pups.

Milk Fever Or Eclampsia

This is a very serious condition and it may be very sudden in onset. It results from a shortage of calcium in the blood stream, and it is usually seen in bitches in poor condition which have had large litters, though it may occur quite unexpectedly in bitches which are plump and well.

symptoms The bitch may appear drowsy, or unsteady on her legs. There is often twitching of the muscles and if no treatment is given convulsions follow. An injection of calcium will usually produce an immediate improvement, so get help at once.

Feeding During Lactation

During the actual whelping the bitch may be offered small drinks of water and glucose, but once the family is complete she will probably feel very hungry and appreciate a bowl of meat broth, or beaten egg and milk. The nutritional requirements of the bitch while feeding her pups are very high indeed, and she can be fed more or less to her capacity, having meals every 4 hours. Even bitches which do not normally like milk will usually take it at this time, so Lactol, milk puddings and cereals can be alternated with the meat meals. It is wise to add a vitamin and mineral supplement to the diet, such as Sherley-Vites. When the pups are being weaned, the amount of food given to the bitch can be gradually reduced.

water

A lack of fluids in the diet will quickly reduce the supply of milk, so see that fresh water is always available to supplement the other drinks.

Rearing And Feeding The Pups

In the first 3 weeks of life the good mother will care for her pups totally. She will not only feed and clean them, but by her constant licking help to ensure that both bladder and bowels are functioning.

3 weeks

At 3 weeks it is wise to start a gradual weaning process to avoid throwing too much strain on the mother especially if there is a large litter. Amongst the best foods to choose are beef broth, with perhaps a few brown bread crumbs added, or one of the sieved baby foods in a meat or chicken flavour. Sherley's Lactol is obviously good, but the pup knows that he can get this more easily from the mother. Put the food on a flattish plate, or dish, and encourage the pups to feed by dipping your finger in the mixture and smearing a little around their mouths. Try to give three meals daily, while the pups are still feeding from the mother as well, and be patient, pups can be exasperatingly clumsy when they first start to feed.

4 weeks

At 4 weeks introduce minced meat or chicken, or flaked fish, as well as Lactol and cereals. Feed each puppy separately to ensure fair shares and prevent a weak pup from being pushed out.

6 weeks

By 6 weeks the pups should be taking 6 meals daily, and taking very little food from the mother (who will probably be beginning to get tired of them). The meals should be three of milky foods, and three of all kinds of meat. Chopped egg can be added to the diet, with a few drops of cod liver oil daily. Fresh water should be available in a heavy flat container that will not tip over easily, or drown an adventurous pup.

By this time the pups will be cutting their first teeth, so a large marrow bone will provide them with a lot of fun. A large strong home-made rag doll will also give them exercise, and keep them out of mischief.

puppy
care

Pups should never be sent to their new homes until they are completely weaned and independent of the mother, if they are to have a fair chance to grow and thrive.

Young pups can easily become infected with fleas and lice, and apart from the obvious irritation and discomfort which they cause, they may result in a considerable deterioration in health and condition. For a purchaser to find that the new puppy is 'lousy' is usually a great shock and reflects badly on the reputation of the breeder. The answer is simple: always examine your pups thoroughly once each week, and give a dusting with an insecticidal dusting powder, taking care to use one that is specifically intended for pups. See chapter 5—External Parasites.

Roundworms can make tiny puppies really ill. The symptoms are usually poor growth, lack of appetite and swollen stomachs.

Treatment can be given quite safely with one of the Sherley's worming preparations, even from as young as 3 weeks, and will need to be repeated several times. See chapter 5—Internal Parasites.

The Bitch At Weaning

Sometimes at weaning a bitch will start to vomit her food. This is probably a reversion to primitive times when the wild dog would regurgitate its half-digested food to feed its pups. It can usually be cured by feeding the bitch in a room well away from the sight and sound of her pups.

If when the pups are completely weaned the bitch still continues to make a lot of milk, you should give Sherley's Milk Suppression Tablets or ask your veterinary surgeon or Animal Welfare Clinic for help with the problem.

Accommodation For The Pups

For the first three weeks the pups will usually be content to stay in the box with their mother, but after that they will start to become adventurous. Try to close off a corner of the room to give the pups an area to play safely without risk of being stepped on. A baby's old play pen is ideal, but you can improvise with fire screens, or old boxes.

Put a tray of sand or litter in a corner, and start to toilet train the pups by putting them there after each feed. Sherley's Swiftie Puppy Trainer will help this process.

As the pups become larger, and more boisterous, it is important also to give the mother the opportunity to get away from them for a little peace!

Rearing Orphan Pups

If you are left with a litter of orphan pups to rear, it is well worth trying first to find a foster mother. The mother dog puts in hours of patient work to keep her pups clean, warm and well fed, so if you are to be the substitute be prepared for some very hard work. Warmth is essential to young pups. The room should be maintained at 80°F. and it is wise to get a thermometer, rather than trust in your own judgement.

In addition there should be a hot water bottle, well wrapped in a woolly cover and kept at a constant temperature, placed in the box itself. The pups will snuggle up to this, and to each other and sleep contentedly.

The box itself should have high sides to prevent the pups climbing out. Put a warm cover (such as part of an old dressing gown) at the sleeping end of the box, and cover the floor with a thick layer of newspaper, which can be easily changed as it is soiled. A lamp of the kind used for rearing baby pigs can be useful to maintain an even heat in the box.

Lactol

Lactol can be used as a complete food for the first 3 weeks, as a substitute for the bitch's milk (given according to the instructions). See the table on page 34 comparing bitch's milk with other milks. At first the pups should be fed every 2-3 hours, but as they start to take more food at a time the intervals can become longer.

An eye dropper can be used as a feeder in an emergency, but a premature baby pipette is usually the most successful method. Make sure that the opening in the teat is large enough to allow the milk to flow easily.

hygiene

Hygiene is of the greatest importance. The orphan pup which has not received the colostrum, or first milk, from the mother, is more susceptible to infections.

After each meal the pups should be wiped over with a piece of damp, clean cotton wool round the face and paws to remove stale food. The stomach should be massaged with a pad of cotton wool to stimulate the action of the bladder and bowels, (in imitation of the licking of the mother dog), and after cleaning with damp gauze or cotton wool the pup should be thoroughly dried, and dusted with a little Maws antiseptic talcum powder, or smeared with a little Vaseline or Maws petroleum jelly if there is any soreness.

A little cornflour added to the food will usually help if there is any diarrhoea, but if it is persistent it is better to get advice. Constipation can usually be remedied by giving one or two drops of liquid paraffin or Lik-A-Med Laxative.

weaning

Orphan pups can usually be weaned quite early, using one of the strained baby foods at first, and their diet can then continue as for normal pups.

Dew-claws And Docking

In most breeds the dew claws are removed (these are the vestigial 'thumbs' of the dog), and in some breeds the tails have to be docked for show purposes. This operation is better carried out by an expert as there is considerable risk of bleeding. It should in all cases be done before the pups are three days old, and it is as well to consult your veterinary surgeon as soon as the pups are born to make the arrangements. This has become a controversial subject and many people feel these operations are not necessary. It would be wise to check requirements with The Kennel Club.

Registering Pedigree Pups

If you are selling your pedigree pups you do not have to register them before sale. However, you must supply the new owners with a completed pedigree form showing the parentage. These forms can usually be obtained from pet shops and it is a good idea to get them and make them out well before you advertise your pups for sale. Sherley's will also supply suitable pedigree forms direct on request.

Chapter 3
CARING FOR
YOUR PUPPY

the new
puppy

The arrival of a new puppy in the home is always an exciting event, especially to children, but remember that the pup will be feeling strange and should be allowed to settle in quietly without too much picking up, or fussing.

Travelling

If you are bringing your puppy home by car don't be surprised if he is sick (but be sure to take a few old newspapers with you). Many pups are upset at their first experience of travel, but in most cases they soon get used to and enjoy the car. It is best to start with short trips, followed by a run in the country, rather than a long journey. For the dog which continues to be sick, Sherley's Travel Sickness Tablets can be of great help.

travel
sickness

A Corner Of His Own

bed or
basket

It is important that the new pet should have his own bed or basket in a quiet, draught-free corner of the room, right from the start. This is his own territory and it will help to give him a sense of security in his new home.

Start at once to teach him the command 'into your basket' and see that it is obeyed. With a young pup it may be necessary to fence off a corner of the room with a strong piece of cardboard, or a fire screen, to confine him to one area. Pups can easily be stepped on and injured if they are allowed the freedom of the house and apart from this danger you will reduce the likelihood of unexpected accidents on your carpets.

chewing

Pups are inveterate chewers, so don't waste money on an expensive dog bed or basket at this stage. You may be astonished at the damage that tiny teeth can cause. A strong cardboard box, with one side cut down, will make a warm and satisfactory first bed, with a piece of old blanket, or a quilted dressing gown—and it can be very cheaply replaced. A fairly thick layer of newspaper at the bottom of the box will give warmth and insulation and it can be discarded daily.

warm and cosy

Place the basket near a radiator if possible, as young pups feel the cold, or supply an old stone hot water bottle, well wrapped up.

It has been suggested that a clock with a loud tick placed near the basket may sound to the puppy like the heart beat of its mother, and provide a little reassurance.

Leaving Your Pup

A puppy which has just left his litter brothers and sisters, and finds itself alone at night for the first time, may well feel lonely and howl. If you are certain that he is not hungry or cold, ignore the noise if you possibly can, although if there are neighbours to consider it is difficult. If you can harden your heart for a few nights, puppy really will get tired of barking but if you once weaken and take him into the bedroom, or worse still, the bed, the battle is lost.

at night

It really is not a kindness to make your pup over dependent on you. A dog which sleeps in its own basket and feels secure there can much more easily be left with friends, or in kennels if it ever becomes necessary.

For the same reason it is wise to make a point of leaving your pup alone in the house for a short time each day (while you go shopping for instance). In this way he will accept being left as the normal thing, and feel confident that you will return.

going shopping

The owner who says 'My dog is devoted to me—I can't leave him anywhere' has simply created an unhappy neurotic pet.

Simple Training

It is no use expecting too much of a young pup in the way of training, but house training, and a few simple commands should be taught, and persevered with.

If you are lucky your pup may have had some house training before his arrival in the home, but if not, prepare to be patient.

house training

Training to newspaper is usually the best method, unless the garden is very close to the kitchen and the weather is good. In any case newspapers will be needed at night as a young puppy cannot be expected to be clean over a period of hours. Put several thicknesses of newspaper on the floor near puppy's basket, and put puppy onto it immediately after feeding, as soon as he wakes up, and indeed on every occasion when you think it may be necessary. Praise him when he uses the paper, and of course scold him if he uses anywhere else. It may sometimes be necessary to lightly smack a pup with a rolled up newspaper if it is constantly disobedient, but a great deal can be achieved by a stern voice. Most pups are anxious to please.

If the puppy does not at once take to the idea of using the newspapers a few drops of Sherley's Swiftie Puppy Trainer sprinkled on the paper will often give him the idea that this is the right place. On the other hand it is important to disinfect thoroughly if the puppy happens to soil the carpets, as dogs tend to return by scent to the same place. Sherley's Savvy Stain Remover will help to remove any soil marks made on soft furnishings. It is better at this stage to confine puppy entirely to a kitchen, where there is an easily washable floor, until clean habits have been established. It is well worth devoting a lot of time to this early training. A puppy which has once learned dirty habits in the house can be very difficult to retrain. As the puppy gets older, and has more bladder and bowel control, start training him to the garden or yard, but remember that you will probably have to continue with newspapers at night for some time.

commands

Keep commands simple at this stage. Pup should learn to go into his box, or basket, and 'stay' when told. Be consistent with your commands, even when you are busy, and see that they are obeyed. Teach pup to come when his name is called, and of course make a fuss of him when he does so. A pup which will not come when he is called is not only a nuisance to his owner, but may be in real danger if he gets loose in traffic.

Calling him by name each meal time will help to teach obedience and associate coming to the call with something pleasant.

**collar and
lead**

Start early to let your pup wear his collar for a short time each day. Some pups resent a collar at first and sulk, but this is an important lesson and you must persevere. A medallion with your name and address is a 'must' as even young pups sometimes stray.

Whether you prefer to use a collar or a harness, or a soft choke lead, you should get your pup used to walking on the lead in the house or garden. Nothing looks worse than to see an unfortunate pup being dragged along the streets by his collar, because he has not been taught to walk properly.

Feeding The Puppy

The main ingredients of a puppy's diet are milk, meat in some form to supply protein, and biscuits or cereal to supply carbohydrates.

milk

Milk is of vital importance to the growing pup, as it supplies the calcium and vitamin D, which are essential for bone formation. It is preferably supplied as Lactol, which is formulated to take the place of the bitch's own milk. See the table on page 34 comparing bitch's milk with other milks.

There is an old wives' tale that giving milk to puppies causes worms. This is quite mistaken. Puppy worms—round worms— are not caused by eating any kind of food, but are directly transmitted from dog to dog.

protein

Protein is usually thought of as being supplied by meat, but fish, eggs and soya beans are also good sources of protein. The main use of protein is to build muscle and body tissues.

Milk contains its own protein (casein) which is of course the only source of protein in the first weeks of a puppy's life. Lactol is extra-rich in protein to match the bitch's milk.

carbohydrates Carbohydrates (starch) are supplied by cereals, biscuits, porridge and bread. This is either used to produce energy and warmth, or stored as fat. For this reason it is better not to give too much biscuit to adult dogs, unless they are really getting hard exercise, or they may develop obesity (over weight)—and fat dogs soon become old dogs. Lactol Meal is an ideal first biscuit food for puppies. Lactol Biscuits and Sherley's Liver Snaps are suitable for older animals.

food needs With puppies there is little danger of overfeeding. Their dietary requirements are very much greater than those of adult dogs, in proportion to their weight. The main growing period in a dog's life is between 7 weeks and 6 months, so it can be understood that it is vital that at this time your puppy is given the right foods in the right amounts. Neglect, or wrong feeding at this time can lead to poor bone formation, bad teeth, or stunting of growth.

It is possible that your puppy will arrive with a diet sheet prepared by his breeder. If this appears to be suiting him, by all means continue with it. If, however, you need to make changes, do so gradually, as young pups, like babies, are easily upset by sudden changes of food.

Age 7-12 weeks. At this stage pups should have 4 small meals in the day, reducing to 3 meals daily towards the end of this period if wished. Two meals should consist of meat in some form. Fresh meat is better minced and may be fed raw or cooked. Chicken or rabbit (cooked and boned) are good, and offal such as liver and heart is nourishing, but may sometimes cause diarrhoea.

Some of the well-known manufacturers of tinned dog foods now pre-pare tinned puppy food, and this may be used according to the manufacturers' instructions. A little puppy meal such as Lactol Meal, or crisp brown bread (dried in the oven) may be added to these two meals for puppies that are eating well. Hard-boiled eggs, or cooked, boned fish may occasionally be substituted for the meat meal.

The other two meals in the day should consist of milk with a little cereal or puppy meal added. Lactol is excellent for this purpose. It is a good idea to provide a large hard biscuit for puppy to chew on, to help with teething. A Lactol Bone is ideal. If you wish to provide a real bone, a really large boiled marrow bone is best. Small or sharp bones are not safe and should never be given.

For puppies, as for adult dogs, fresh water should be always available.

From 12 weeks-6 months. Three meals daily are usually sufficient, increasing the quantities proportionately as puppy grows. Usually the first meal or breakfast is the milky one and the other two are of meat and biscuit. If pup seems to get tired of cereals and milk give just a drink of milk with a rusk or hard biscuit in the morning.

From 6 months-1 year. Two meals daily should be the practice. These may be morning and evening or mid-day and evening, according to the dog's appetite, or to suit the owner's way of life. By this age both meals are of meat and biscuit, but by all means continue with a small drink of milk daily, if your dog enjoys it.

Quantities To Feed

This is a very difficult subject to generalise on, as puppies of the different breeds obviously vary greatly in size. As a guide-line, a puppy which is being fed 4 times daily can be given as much food as it will clear up straight away at each mealtime.

regular routine

Start with a tablespoonful and increase as necessary. If your puppy is well and active, and food is being left, you are almost certainly overfeeding. If, however, your puppy is not taking its food, and seems quiet and listless, you would be wise to consult your veterinary surgeon. Try to keep to regular mealtimes. A pup has a small stomach capacity and will thrive much better on frequent small meals than on one large one. If any food is left, don't leave it on the floor to harbour germs, but take it up straight away. Some pups enjoy green vegetables, and a little may be added to the food daily if wished.

Cod liver oil and vitamin and mineral supplements may be needed for a pup which is in poor condition. Sherley-Vites, Sherley's Lintox Tonic and Sherley's Cod Liver Oil Capsules are all suitable. It is important to give these strictly according to the manufacturer's instructions. An overdose may be just as harmful as an underdose.

Teething

Your pup will have a complete set of sharp puppy teeth when he arrives—as you will probably soon find out.

puppy teeth

Between the ages of 12 weeks and 6 months he will gradually shed his puppy teeth, and cut his permanent, or adult teeth. The first permanent teeth to come through are usually the two centre teeth on the top jaw, and the last are the big corner or canine teeth in the top and bottom jaw. This gives a reasonably accurate idea of a puppy's age from an examination of its mouth. Most puppies change their teeth with very little discomfort, but occasionally there may be some soreness or bleeding.

In a few cases, and more often in the miniature breeds, the puppy's teeth are not shed before the permanent teeth start to come through. This not only causes discomfort to the pup, but may spoil the shape of the mouth so if this occurs it is best to consult a veterinary surgeon.

While the teething process is going on, pups tend to chew *everything* so learn to be tidy. Never leave shoes, or indeed anything chewable,

chewing

within puppy's reach—and don't give pup an old shoe as a

plaything. He cannot be expected to distinguish the old from the new. Provide a really large boiled marrow bone that pup can chew at without harm, give one or two really hard biscuits like a Lactol Bone, to play with, or make a really strong rag doll, by stitching together several old sweaters. Dog chews, made from hardened hide are safe, and most pups enjoy them. Sherley's Stop Chew can be sprayed on favourite spots to deter chewing.

Grooming And Bathing

Puppies don't usually need to be bathed, but if it should be necessary, use lukewarm water, a mild dog shampoo—choose one from the Sherley's range listed in Chapter 8—and take care to see that the puppy is thoroughly dried and not allowed to become chilled.

brushing

Brushing and combing should be carried out daily, especially with the long coated varieties. It is never too soon to start good habits. A fairly soft nylon brush is often best at this stage.

fleas

Puppies, even from the best of homes, may sometimes have fleas. There is no need to be unduly alarmed about this, as dog fleas do not live on humans. However, a dusting once weekly with a mild insecticidal powder like Sherley's No Scratch, and regular washing of the bedding will keep your pup free from these troubles (see also Chapter 5 on External Parasites).

Your Puppy's Health

vaccination

Vaccination against the four major infectious diseases of dogs is the most important step you should take to guaranteee your pup's health.

These diseases are: **Distemper** (including what is sometimes called hard pad disease)—the distemper virus is the cause of the worst killer disease of dogs; **Hepatitis**—a serious liver disease caused by another virus; **Jaundice**—a particularly unpleasant disease caused by leptospira; and a form of **Nephritis**—a kidney disease caused by another type of leptospira.

Vaccination against these four diseases can be accomplished by one series of injections. Never put off vaccination, either from thoughtlessness, or from reasons of economy, because this neglect could cost your dog's life.

isolation

Puppies should be kept in their own homes prior to vaccination, and isolated from contact with other dogs to prevent infection. Virus diseases are extremely infectious, and may be picked up from the ground, even without actual contact with another dog. Any grass verge, where other dogs are walked can be a potential source of infection.

age for vaccination

Vaccination is usually carried out at about 12 weeks of age, or younger. It is best to get in touch with your local veterinary surgeon to make arrangements as soon as you get your new puppy.

Most pups have some roundworms, even though they may have come from a good home and have had some previous treatment.

It is a good idea to dose the puppy routinely at regular intervals with a Sherley's worming preparation, in his early life, both for his own sake, and to avoid any risk of infection to children. Worms may cause illness in young pups, but if your pup is listless or off his food, don't conclude that this is the cause, without consulting a veterinary surgeon. Modern worm remedies are very safe for a healthy pup, but they would not be helpful if your pup is in the early stages of an infectious disease. (The subject of worming is covered in detail in Chapter 5 on Internal Parasites).

A healthy pup should be ready for its meals, and clear them up at once. It should have a shiny coat, and bright eyes, and be plump, without being over-fat. It should be lively and alert and ready to play. If your pup answers to this description you have got off to a good start.

Lactol

Because puppies grow very rapidly compared to a calf, bitch's milk is much richer than cow's milk. It contains 3 times as much fat, twice as much casein (a protein), 10 times as much albumin (another protein) and less sugar and water, compared to cow's milk.

Puppies that are being artificially fed will not thrive on cow's milk, as they do not receive enough fat or protein and have to take too much sugar and water. Even puppies which only receive cow's milk as a supplement to the diet can experience gastric problems because of the imbalance.

Lactol is specially formulated to match bitch's milk as closely as possible and is more suitable for puppies than any other preparation. It is also ideal for pregnant and nursing bitches.

Average Analysis of Various Milks

		Fat	Casein etc.	Albu-min	Milk Sugar	Ash	Total Solids	Water	Specific Gravity
Cow	—	3.73	3.04	0.54	4.90	0.71	12.92	87.08	1.0310
Bitch	—	9.57	6.10	5.05	3.08	0.73	24.53	75.47	1.0350
Ewe	—	6.86	4.97	1.55	4.91	0.89	19.18	80.82	1.0400
Mare	—	1.20	1.90	0.10	5.70	0.40	9.30	90.70	1.0374
Cat	—	3.33	3.12	5.93	4.91	0.58	17.90	82.10	
Goat	—	4.78	3.20	1.09	4.46	0.76	14.29	85.71	1.0335
Sow	—	4.55	7.23		3.13	1.05	15.96	84.09	1.0380

CARING FOR YOUR DOG

Taking on an adult dog as a pet may be something of a gamble. He may have been well brought up, and be thoroughly obedient, in which case you will have avoided all the work and trouble of housetraining and discipline. On the other hand, he may have been allowed to run wild and you will have a very difficult task ahead to train him into your ways. It may happen that out of kindness, you inherit a pet from a friend or relative who cannot keep it, and if it is no longer young you will probably have to accept, and live with, its faults. However, if you plan to buy an adult dog, or answer an advertisement for one wanting a good home, do try to find out why the last owner is parting with it. It may turn out to chase motor cycles, bite people or kill chickens—do not take on someone else's problems unless you are really used to dogs, and feel able to deal with them. It is no kindness to the problem dog if he is to be passed from one home to another. If you have a dog that is vicious, or out of control, do not pass him onto someone who wants a guard dog. Many of these so-called guard dogs lead wretched lives, chained to a cold draughty kennel all day. If a dog is really unmanageable it is better to have him painlessly destroyed.

His Own Corner In The House

The adult dog, like the pup, should always have his own box, or basket, placed in a quiet draught-free corner of the room and he should learn from the start to go into his basket, and stay there, when told.

Do not let your dog sit on the chairs, or if you must, then see that he has one old chair that is his own. You may not mind having your clothes covered in dogs' hair, but it can be very hard on unsuspecting visitors.

What Kind Of Bed?

Now that your dog has—we hope—passed the stage of chewing things, it is time to choose a suitable bed. You may decide on the traditional basket, but a strong wooden box, with one side cut down, is equally good. In either case the bed should be large enough for the dog to stretch out comfortably and should be provided with a thick piece of blanket as a mattress. It is worth remembering that the eggs of fleas are shed in the bedding so see that the dog blankets are washed regularly. Canvas beds, on a metal frame, are comfortable and easy to keep clean, and they fold away for travelling. Plastic is used both to make a basket type bed, or to cover a padded metal frame, to make a more comfortable and draught free bed.

clean bedding

Kennels

If your dog is to live in a kennel make sure that it is warm and weather-proof. It should be constructed of wood, and should be raised off the ground to avoid damp and draughts. Except in very good weather, it is preferable that the kennel should be placed inside another building, such as a garage or shed.

If the kennel is to serve as a permanent home for the dog it should be large enough to contain a raised bench type bed, and should stand in its own concrete run, in some part of the garden protected from cold winds or hot sun.

Straw may be used as bedding and it is best burned after use.

disinfection

The droppings should be removed from the kennel run daily to avoid build up of worm infestation and the whole floor area swilled out with disinfectant. The benches should be scrubbed with disinfectant at least weekly.

Exercise

Adequate exercise is of the greatest importance in keeping a dog happy and healthy, indeed many of the illnesses of dogs—and men—can be traced back to too much food and too little exercise. By adequate exercise is meant at least one hour daily, for all except the really toy breeds and more if possible, and let it be a good run off the lead, not a dreary trail round streets, or worse still, shops. If you find this impossible to manage, a good game with a ball will help to tire out the dog without tiring its owner too much.

walks and runs

Training

Exercising your dog will only be a pleasure if he has learned at least the rudiments of discipline and training. If you have brought your dog up from a puppy, the training programme should be fairly easy. He should have learned the one important lesson that when you give

commands

36

an order you really mean it. Half-hearted commands leave the dog feeling uncertain, and, like children, they are inclined to get away with as much as they can. With a dog of 6 months or over behaviour patterns have been built up, and training is much more difficult, and requires endless patience.

Walking On The Lead

It is only too common to see dog owners being dragged round the streets by their dogs—making passers-by wonder who is taking whom for a walk. This sort of behaviour is really quite unnecessary. A puppy should be accustomed to walking on the lead from a very early age. If he attempts to pull on the lead, pull him back sharply until he is walking at your side. If he does not respond promptly, tap him on the nose with a rolled newspaper and pull him back. Never, even if you are busy, or in a hurry, let him get away with dragging on the lead, or the value of the lesson is lost.

pulling on the lead

With an older dog who has got into the habit of pulling, you will need to be more severe. Use a choke chain type of collar to help you control him. Speak to him very sharply, and pull him back to the level of your legs each time that he pulls, giving him a tap with the rolled paper if necessary. When your dog has become used to walking quite nicely on the lead, try teaching him to walk 'at heel' off the lead. Choose a quiet place for this lesson, away from distractions and, of course, away from traffic. Make him halt and sit at road crossings, and never cross until he gets the word of command.

traffic

It is not wise to allow even a well-trained dog to walk off the lead on a road where there is busy traffic. A sudden distraction, such as a dog on the other side of the road, may cause him to forget his training with fatal results.

cleanliness

If you live in a town, never allow your dog to foul the pavement. Walk him along the outside of the pavement, and step out into the gutter as soon as you think that he is about to defecate, taking care to see that he is not so far out in the road as to be in danger from passing cars.

Finally, and it should not be necessary to say, never turn your dog out to take a run on his own, even though you may feel that you live in a quiet situation. This not only shows a callous disregard for your dog's welfare, but may be the cause of a serious accident.

"come"

Every dog should learn to come when called by name, or to a whistle, otherwise exercising off the lead becomes a hazard and a danger.

Start training in a confined space, in the house or garden. Call your dog to you in an encouraging tone of voice and make a great fuss of him when he comes. Do this three or four times each day, but don't continue too long or he will become bored.

If he is slow to learn this lesson, put him on a length of clothes line, and pull him sharply towards you as you call and then, of course, praise him when he comes.

With older dogs that have not learned to come to a call it may be necessary to use a piece of cheese, meat or Lactol Drops as reward, but it is better not to start this system if it can be avoided.

Never chase after your dog, or puppy, if he runs away. This soon becomes a game to him, and you will find that he can run much faster than you. If you are outside, call him in an encouraging tone of voice, bending, or kneeling on the ground, and holding your arms out. In an emergency it is sometimes effective to call your dog, while running in the opposite direction, to distract him from crossing a busy road, or some other danger. Finally, however exasperated you may be feeling, do not scold your dog when he finally does come back. He will only be more reluctant to return next time.

"sit" and "stay"

Teach your dog to 'sit' by pressing him firmly down on the hindquarters, while repeating the command in a fairly stern voice. When this lesson has been thoroughly mastered, tell him to 'sit', then 'stay' while you walk a few paces away. If he attempts to follow you speak to him sternly, and put him back in his place. Gradually increase the distance and then try moving just out of his sight, preferably in such a way that you can still see him, and call out 'stay' if he starts to move.

Make your dog sit while you prepare his meal every day, then wait until he hears the command to come.

It is a good idea to get in the habit of opening your dog's mouth, so that if it is ever necessary to examine his mouth, or to give medicine, he does not resent handling.

Good Manners In The House

If your dog is to be a pleasure to you he must learn 'polite manners' in the house. He will of course by now have learned to be clean in the house. Nervous puppies may still sometimes urinate if there is some excitement, or if a visitor calls, but this is fairly normal, and is a habit that they will soon grow out of. It is better not to rebuke them sharply as this simply makes a timid puppy even more so.

visitors

Your dog should also have learned to go into his own bed when told and stay there, not to commandeer the best chair in the house, with his feet covered with mud. You may want your pup to learn to be a watch dog, but do train him to give a warning only when strangers approach, not to go on and on barking. Do not let your dog jump up to greet you, or your friends. This may sound harsh advice, but muddy paws or torn stockings are not pleasant. Bend down to stroke your dog, and speak to him firmly if he jumps up, saying 'down' in a stern voice.

titbits

Adolescent dogs, when they become excited, will often attempt to mount strange dogs, or the legs of visitors. This rather embarrassing habit should be checked, saying 'down' in a firm voice, or giving a sharp tap if necessary. Dogs soon become aware of what is acceptable behaviour. Never feed your dog at the table. You have only yourself to blame if he makes a nuisance of himself by begging at mealtimes. If you want to give him the scraps, put them into his own dish, and give them at the proper feeding time. And of course never start the bad habit of giving sweets to your dog. They are bad for his teeth and his figure—and we all know of dogs who spring to life when they hear a sweet paper rustle. Sweets are not a natural, or a necessary item of your dog's diet, and if you don't start the bad habit, he will never miss them.

Teaching Tricks

Some dogs, such as poodles, have a natural aptitude for learning tricks and seem to enjoy them, but as a general rule this is not something that should be encouraged.

Tricks such as begging, or walking on the hind legs may be positively harmful, especially in the long bodied type of dog. There is always the danger that they may overbalance, causing injury to the spine.

It is better to let your dog lead a happy 'dog's life' rather than try to make him into a substitute human.

Training Classes

For dogs that prove really difficult to train it is well worth considering attending dog training classes. These are held in many districts now, very often under the auspices of the local police. They are particularly helpful because they teach the owner how to train his, or her, own dog. One word of warning though: it is important to carry on with the training programme at home as well.

Some people send their dogs away to be trained. This can sometimes be successful, but only too often a dog which has worked well with a trainer comes home and immediately reverts to its previous bad behaviour. This probably points to the truth that there are bad owners, as well as bad dogs.

specialised training

There are also specialised types of training classes for the different breeds. Alsatian and labrador breed societies organise obedience training classes; labradors, spaniels, retrievers and other sporting breeds can attend field trials, and bloodhounds can be taught tracking. All these are sensible ways of making the most of your dog's natural intelligence, and they can provide a satisfying hobby for the owner.

Grooming And Routine Dog Care

All dogs need regular grooming. It improves the appearance of short coated varieties and it is absolutely essential for those with long and curly coats. It also does much to minimise the amount of hair shed on furniture and carpets. Start as you mean to go on. If you get your puppy used to a daily grooming from an early age he will accept it as a normal routine, and as a rule get to enjoy it.

grooming equipment

For short haired varieties a fairly firm close clothes brush is usually best. It will remove the loose hair and give a shine to the coat. A rubber glove stroked firmly down the coat will also help to remove excess hair, especially in the moulting season, and a final polish with a soft duster will give a nice finish to the grooming. For long haired

39

breeds a strong steel comb and a long bristled brush are essential. So many owners think that they are grooming their dogs when they are actually only running a brush over the surface of the tangles. A daily grooming should prevent the formation of matts and tangles, even in spaniels and poodles, but if they have been allowed to form, it is best to cut them out with scissors. Use a blunt-ended pair of scissors, a good light, and care—and don't worry about the bare places, the hair will soon grow again. If you tug away at painful tangles your dog will soon dread the sight of the brush, and grooming will become an ordeal to be avoided.

parasites Remember while grooming your dog to look for parasites such as fleas and lice which may have been picked up—and to deal with them appropriately (see Chapter 5 dealing with External Parasites).

You may also find grass seeds in the coat, and especially between the toes. These, if not removed, may penetrate the skin causing painful abscesses. A daily examination of the coat will also give you the opportunity to check for any signs of scurf, or skin irritations, that may need attention.

foot care The feet should be examined daily, especially in hairy types of dogs, such as spaniels, for the presence of thorns. It is better to keep the hair between the toes and under the pads, trimmed short, and to wash the feet after exercise in muddy weather. The accumulation of grit and and hard packed mud under the pads may contribute to the formation of interdigital cysts or boils on the feet. These are most commonly seen in dogs which have deep 'wells' under the toes, which collect mud; regular care of the feet can do much to avoid this trouble.

Nail Cutting

Dogs which live in the town usually get sufficient exercise on hard ground to keep their nails short, and indeed in some cases the nails may become worn too far down, and consequently painful. However,

Diagram of dog's foot showing a claw. The shaded area is the very sensitive quick.

dew-claws

dogs living in the country, or being exercised mainly on soft ground may often require a manicure. It is important to remember that the nail of the dog has a very sensitive 'quick' and it is only the hard, horny tip that is to be trimmed. Use a strong pair of nail cutters, and little and often is the best policy to follow. You will hurt your dog if you cut the nail too short, and there may well be considerable bleeding—and you must not be surprised if your dog is very apprehensive when a manicure is necessary again. The dew-claws should not be forgotten when trimming the nails. These extra claws or thumbs are situated on the inner aspect of the legs, sometimes on the front paws only, but sometimes on the back also. They are of no use to the civilised dog, and indeed they are often removed soon after birth. Because they do not wear at all, they may sometimes become ingrowing and cause the dog considerable distress before the cause of the trouble is realised. They are also inclined to become caught and broken, if they are too long, leaving a painful exposed quick.

Bathing

While regular grooming can do a great deal to keep a dog's coat looking clean and trim, from time to time a bath becomes necessary. White dogs which live in the town need fairly frequent bathing if they are not to become grey dogs; and dogs which have the unfortunate habit of rolling on anything disagreeable that they can find, become frequent candidates for the tub. However, apart from this, any dog which lives as one of the family will smell sweeter and feel fresher for the occasional bath. Using lukewarm water, and a reliable dog shampoo, such as one from the Sherley's or Amplex range, lather the dog all over, rinse well, and then repeat the process. The final rinse should be very thorough, to remove all traces of shampoo from the hair, or the coat will be left with a dull scurfy appearance. A hair spray attachment for the tap makes this job easier. Particular care should be taken when washing the head to avoid getting any lather in the eyes. A little Vaseline smeared over the lids will act as a protection.

lather
and rinse

Remove most of the moisture from the coat by rubbing with a dry towel, then complete the process with an electric hair dryer, provided that the dog is not frightened by it or keep the dog in a warm place until it is completely dry.

A final brush through the coat and you will have a dog to be proud of.

medicated
baths

Medicated baths may sometimes be necessary for the treatment of fleas, etc. These should be carried out strictly according to the manufacturer's instructions. Sherley's Insecticidal Shampoo is very straightforward to use.

Ears

The ears should be examined daily as part of the grooming routine. Long-eared breeds, such as spaniels and poodles seem much more susceptible to ear trouble than the prick-eared breeds, probably because the flap of the ear prevents adequate ventilation of the ear canal. This another example of the way in which man has caused

ear care

quite unnecessary troubles to the dog, by breeding for appearance, instead of for soundness and health.

The ears may be cleaned if it is necessary, to remove accumulations of wax. The best method is to wipe out the ears gently, using a little cotton wool and a few drops of liquid paraffin or olive oil. It is not wise for an inexperienced person to use any kind of a probe to clean the ears, as the delicate inner surface of the ears may easily be damaged, especially if the dog jumps unexpectedly. If your dog **grass seeds** suddenly develops a painful ear (shown usually by holding the head on one side, crying, or shaking his head) especially following a walk in the grass, he may have a grass seed, or barley awn in the ear. These are difficult to remove without expert advice so it is best to consult a veterinary surgeon.

Persistent shaking of the head may also indicate that your dog has picked up lice or ear mites, and these of course should be dealt with (See Chapter 5 on External Parasites).

An unpleasant or unusual smell from the ears, or any sign of discharge may indicate an infection and it is best to obtain some professional advice.

eye care Generally no specific eye care is needed and any eye problem will soon be obvious; it will probably require professional treatment. One related problem often seen by owners of light coloured dogs, is a tear stain down the side of the nose; the ideal way to clean this (for cosmetic reasons) is Sherley's Tear Stain Remover.

The teeth should be examined occasionally and cleaned if the dog will allow. Examination may show particles of bone that have lodged in the teeth, or sometimes pieces of stick, if the dog likes to play with them. It will also show any bad teeth that may be causing pain or needing attention. Deposits of tartar sometimes build up on the **teeth** teeth, mainly on the outer surfaces and this, if it becomes noticeable, should be chipped or scaled away. A placid dog may allow you to do this at home, but if in doubt it is best to consult a veterinary surgeon. For regular cleaning of dogs' teeth it is best to use cotton wool damped, and dipped in tooth powder, or a little hydrogen peroxide, available from the chemist. Rub over the teeth, then rinse well with clean water. Most dogs object a little at first, but they become accustomed to the treatment and the results are very rewarding, in the form of cleaner teeth and sweeter breath. It is wiser not to use a brush to clean your dog's teeth as you may cause sore gums if he jumps unexpectedly.

Trimming And Stripping

Many breeds of dogs, such as terriers, all of the rough coated varieties—this includes west highlands, scotties, airedales and wire haired fox terriers—and spaniels, require trimming, usually twice in the year, in spring and autumn, to get rid of their old coats and to keep them looking trim and tidy. Poodles, on the other hand, have a very rapidly growing coat and need to be trimmed every 6 weeks, if they are not to look like old sheep. This can obviously involve the owner in a lot of expense, and it is well worth learning to do the job yourself. You may never manage to achieve more than a neat appearance, but unless the dog is being shown, this is quite sufficient, and for a nervous dog, it is much less upsetting than being left at a poodle parlour.

terriers Terriers have a tough hard coat, which should correctly be trimmed by pulling, or plucking the loose hard hair. This is very laborious work unless you are an expert, so for a beginner it is a good idea to use either a trimming comb—a comb with an attached replaceable blade—and a pair of scissors, or to go to the initial expense of a good pair of electric clippers. A terrier when correctly trimmed should have a rather square, or box-like appearance. It is a good idea to get a picture of a show specimen from a magazine.

spaniels Spaniels should also be stripped using either a stripping knife, or a stripping comb. The coat should have a smooth silky appearance when finished, the ears should be thinned out and the feather on the legs should only be thinned and evened, not cut. Spaniels may be trimmed with electric clippers, but great care is needed to get a satisfactory, even appearance.

poodles Poodles are best trimmed with scissors only. Many people use clippers in the interest of speed, but poodles have sensitive skins, and if the hair is cut too close, painful areas of clipping rash may occur, especially over the neck, and sides of the face, which can be very slow to heal. For poodle trimming you will need a strong, sharp pair of pointed trimming scissors, a strong steel comb, with fairly close teeth, and a stiff brush. If you have groomed your dog regularly the job will be easy, but in any case there are no short cuts. If the finished results are to be satisfactory you must comb out all tangles before you start to cut.

style By far the most popular, sensible, and from the dog's point of view, comfortable, poodle trim is the lamb trim. In this the feet, muzzle, and base of tail are trimmed close, and the body coat is trimmed fairly short and even all over. Moustaches may be left if you wish. A puppy trim is very similar, but the body coat is left longer as a protection against the weather. The more elaborate trims are the lion, Dutch and continental. These are really only justifiable for those who want to show their dogs. The average owner wants a happy, clean neat dog, not a fashion plate. See illustrations on next page.

Bedlington terriers have woolly coats rather like poodles, and they are trimmed with scissors. The style is very much like a lamb, and again it is essential to get a picture of one correctly trimmed to use as a pattern.

Retrievers and collies are not trimmed at all, but they can be much improved by a really thorough grooming, and having the hair thinned with a trimming comb.

Puppy trim.   *Lamb trim.*

Lion trim.

Dutch or modern trim.   *Continental trim.*

Hygiene And Disinfection

1. All dogs should be groomed daily, and dusted with an insecticide powder such as Vamoose if there is any risk of infestation with fleas or lice.

2. Bedding or blankets should be regularly washed.

six points

3. Exercise areas should be kept clean, and disinfected where possible. Dogs, and especially puppies, shed round worm eggs and there is risk of re-infection.

4. Following any case of skin disease such as ringworm, or mange, it is of the greatest importance to destroy all bedding, including the box or basket. Do not forget the collar and lead as well.

5. Distemper (including hard pad) is one of the most persistent infections. If there has been a case in a house remember that the virus can remain alive on furniture and carpets for a considerable time. It is wiser not to introduce an un-inoculated puppy into a house where there has been a case of distemper.

6. Let your dog have his own food dishes and see that they are kept separate and washed daily.

The Correct Diet For Your Dog

nutrition

The dog is a carnivore and in the wild state meat was his normal diet, but it should be realised that at this time he usually ate the whole of his kill to supply the protein, fats, minerals and vitamins that he needed. Today, when there is a world-wide shortage of meat—apart from its increase in price—substitutes for the protein part of a dog's diet must be found, and these include not only fish, eggs, and cheese, but also vegetable protein such as that derived from the soya bean. Large dogs, and especially working dogs or those which get a considerable amount of exercise, are able to utilise quite a lot of carbohydrates in their diet in the form of biscuits or meal to supply energy and warmth. It is difficult to generalise about the quantities of food which should be fed to a dog, as even within the different breeds there are great differences in the individual requirements. It is worth remembering though that if you are feeding more food than the dog needs to replace tissues, and to supply heat and energy for the body, it will be stored as fat, and a fat dog is not usually a fit, or happy one. It is equally true to say that a dog which is underfed will lose weight, but it is perhaps a tribute to our kind hearts that overweight is now much more of a problem in dogs.

quantity to feed

The dog is naturally adapted to eating at fairly infrequent intervals, and the food tends to remain in the stomach for a considerable time before digestion takes place. For the adult healthy dog, one or two meals are quite sufficient, given as far as possible at a regular time each day. Do not get into the habit of leaving a plate of biscuits down for your dog to nibble at through the day. It is not necessary if

time to feed

he is receiving a properly balanced diet, and the habit of eating through the day is as bad for a dog's figure as for ours.

Never give your dog scraps at meal times, or worse still, feed him at the table. If he is to be given the scraps put them in his own dish, and give them at the proper time.

A dog which perpetually begs at the table is a nuisance (and his owner is to blame), and a dog which gets extras throughout the day will often be faddy and refuse his meals. A healthy dog, which is getting sufficient exercise, and the right quantity of food, should be ready for its meals and clear them up at once. If your dog is choosy about the foods he will eat you are probably overfeeding him. Cut down drastically on the quantities you are offering for a few days, and his appetite will usually improve. On the other hand if a normally hungry dog suddenly refuses his food this may be a sign of illness. If it continues for more than 24 hours he probably needs professional attendance.

sweets and treats

Do not start the bad habit of giving sweets or chocolate to your dog. They are not necessary and they may damage his teeth. A piece of cheese makes a better reward if it is necessary in training.

what to feed

The meal will usually consist of part meat (or protein in some form) and part biscuit, the quantities of each varying according to the weight, age and the amount of daily exercise. A pregnant bitch, or a growing pup may require considerably more food relative to its size than a normal adult dog. Equally a dog living in a very cold climate will require extra food to maintain its body heat, and a collie running all day on the hills will need more to supply energy.

A small dog may take meat only at the meal, with the addition of a hard biscuit or two to help the teeth. The meal for a large dog may consist of half biscuit and half meat. It is better to feed the biscuit fairly dry to give the dog something firm to chew on. Any gravy should be added at the last minute.

protein

The protein part of your dog's diet may consist of fresh meat, if it is available. It may be fed raw if it is absolutely fresh, but if there is any risk of contamination by flies it is better to boil it for a short time. If meat is to be stored in a refrigerator see that it is brought to room temperature before giving it to your dog, or you may find an attack of colic or stomach-ache is the result.

offal

Liver, heart, and kidneys have excellent food value, but in some dogs they may cause diarrhoea, so feed them cautiously at first. Tripe is a useful food, but lights, although they are very palatable to dogs, are low in food value.

other foods

Fish, rabbit, or chicken are useful sources of protein and particularly valuable as invalid food, but great care should be taken to remove all bones. Eggs may be given if wished and beaten egg and milk makes a good tonic for a pregnant bitch or a dog in poor condition. Vegetables such as carrots or green vegetables may be included in a dog's diet if wished, but they are not essential.

Today a great proportion of our dogs is fed partly, or in whole, on prepared dog foods. Those prepared by the leading manufacturers are very carefully formulated to supply all the nutrients required for a dog's health and although they are on the face of it fairly expensive to buy, there is no waste, and the actual value may compare well with meat bought from the butcher. Prepared foods may come in the form of tinned foods, which usually have a high moisture content, the new semi-moist foods prepared in packets, or sachets, or as a biscuit with a variable meat content, but usually with a high carbohydrate value.

Care should be taken to check with the manufacturer's description as to whether the food is an all-meat product, or if it contains a proportion of cereal as well.

Dogs certainly enjoy bones and they do have some value in keeping the teeth clean, but they should be given only with caution. Really large marrow bones when they are available are excellent, but any bones which the dog can break up and splinter are dangerous. Sharp bones such as chicken or rabbit should never be given, and small bones, such as chops are equally dangerous. They can only too easily be swallowed whole and they may become lodged at the entrance to the stomach, or in the intestine, with sometimes fatal results. Soft bones such as pork, or breast of lamb are less dangerous, but when chewed up and swallowed they form a hard concrete-like mass in the bowel and may cause a bad case of constipation. It is worth mentioning that a dog which has eaten a bone will normally pass a very characteristic hard whitish motion.

You may possibly be thinking that dogs in the wild state must have eaten bones and this is obviously true, but a certain number of them died as a result, and you would not wish this to happen to your pet.

Dog chews or mock bones made from hide are useful for the dog who really loves something to chew, or for puppies which are cutting teeth, and they are free from the disadvantages of real bones.

Travel

Most dogs love to travel by car once they become accustomed to it; indeed many dogs seem to be happy just to sit in a stationary car, pretending it is going along. However, if the journey is to be a pleasure for both dog and owner too, it is important that your dog
should learn good car manners. Let him have his own place on the seat, or on the floor, with his own rug. Do not allow him to leap from front to back of the car when something attracts his attention outside, or to hang his head out of the window. The first is very dangerous for the driver, and the second is liable to cause sore eyes. A good dog barrier for the rear of an estate car is a sound investment.

A dog bag is a very useful thing to keep in the car. This is shaped like a pillow case, in a size appropriate to the dog, and made of strong towelling or any strong material. You can pop your dog into it after a muddy walk, fastening it around the neck if necessary. By the
time you get home you will have a drier, cleaner dog, and clean car.

car sickness

Many dogs or puppies are sick at their first experience of car travel, but in most cases they soon get over it, especially if they are only taken on short journeys at first, with a nice run at the end. For the dog which is persistently sick extra care must be taken. Give a short walk before the journey, and do not give a meal for at least 2 hours before.

Sherley's Travel Sickness Tablets given well before leaving will usually produce a great improvement both for dogs which suffer from sickness and for those which are nervous or excitable in a car.

train travel

If you are travelling by train you may be allowed to keep your dog with you in the compartment, but you may be asked to produce a muzzle, or to place him in the guard's van, at the discretion of the train staff.

Sending puppies or dogs unaccompanied by train is something to be avoided if possible. In spite of all your care and precautions, mistakes and delays can occur, and a lonely, hungry puppy is left sitting on a station many miles from its proper destination. If you want to buy a puppy from some distance away, it is well worth the time and expense to fetch it yourself.

If puppies are to be sent by train, they should be placed in a sufficiently large and well ventilated crate, with good clearly written labels, indicating both the sender, and the recipient. Send them by passenger train, and ensure that the person to whom they are sent is on the platform to receive the crate, or to notify you at once if it doesn't arrive.

air travel

Whether travelling with you, or unaccompanied, your dog or pup will have to travel in a crate in the luggage compartment of the plane. This is liable to be both noisy and cold, so it is as well to provide a warm blanket, and in the case of a nervous dog to give a Sherley's Sedative Tablet. If you are travelling abroad with your dog the firm which is arranging your transport will usually take care of the arrangements for your dog as well. If you are sending a dog on its own you will be wise to put yourself in the hands of a firm specialising in this work (such as Spratt's or Lep).

Quarantine Regulations

All dogs entering either the United Kingdom or Ireland are required to undergo 6 months isolation in a quarantine kennel. This may sound harsh, but it is an essential precaution to prevent the introduction of rabies into this country. Rabies is not only a dreadful disease of dogs, but the bite from a 'rabid' dog causes a terrible and fatal disease in man. The period between the original infection and the development of symptoms of the disease may be as long as 6 months, and this is why the quarantine must be so long. The United Kingdom and Ireland are free from rabies as a result of these very strict regulations, but remember if you ever feel tempted to smuggle a dog into the country you are not only breaking the law and risking a heavy fine, but you may be responsible for causing an outbreak of

rabies

rabies which could cost not only the lives of many dogs, but many people and wild animals as well.

six
months
The importation of dogs (and cats) into Great Britain from abroad is controlled by the Ministry of Agriculture, Fisheries and Food, Government Buildings, Hook Rise South, Tolworth, Surbiton, Surrey, or in Scotland, by the Department of Agriculture and Fisheries for Scotland, Chesser House, 500 Gorgie Road, Edinburgh EH11 3AW. No dogs may be landed without a licence previously obtained for them. All such licences require the animals to undergo detention and isolation for six months on Government Authorised Quarantine Premises and to be twice vaccinated after arrival there with an approved anti-rabies vaccine. Imported dogs must be conveyed from the port of entry to the place of detention by authorised Carrying Agents. A list of Carrying Agents can be obtained from the Ministry. Any performing dogs brought into the country will have to continue to meet normal quarantine requirements.

Similar conditions are imposed by the Authorities concerned in Eire, Northern Ireland and the Channel Islands, whilst dogs imported from abroad may not enter the Isle of Man until they have completed the requisite six months' quarantine in Great Britain, in Eire, or in Northern Ireland.

Provided that they are not actually subject to quarantine restrictions owing to their recent importation from abroad, dogs may be moved freely between and within Great Britain, Northern Ireland, Eire, the Channel Islands, and the Isle of Man.

Taking Your Dog Abroad

When taking your dog out of the United Kingdom you will require a certificate of health given by a veterinary surgeon within a few days of leaving. In addition, some countries require your dog to be vaccinated against rabies, or to produce a certificate showing that it is free from leptospirosis (kidney disease). In some countries there is a short quarantine period on arrival, but because the United Kingdom is free from rabies most places will admit British dogs at once. It really is important to find out all these details about the country concerned as soon as possible. Failure to do this may involve you in considerable delay, or heartbreak, if you find that you are unable to take your pet with you.

Putting Your Dog In Kennels

If your circumstances make it probable that you will have to put your dog in kennels from time to time, it is as well to get him used to it as early in his life as possible. Young dogs, if they have been sensibly brought up to be reasonably independent, will usually take to kennel life quite well. An older dog, which has only known its own home is more likely to be distressed and to feel that you have left it for ever. Do go and see the kennels for yourself, in good time before your holidays. If they are clean and well run you can have an easy
inspect the
kennels
mind, and if they are not you have time to make other arrangements. It is no use deciding when your plane is just about to

leave, that the place is quite unsuitable. Let your dog take his own bed and blanket with him, so that he feels less isolated and far from home. Check that the food at the kennels is something that he is used to, or offer to take a supply of his regular food. Most conscientious kennel proprietors now require a certificate of distemper vaccination, so check in good time to see if your dog requires a booster injection: this is usually given annually. It is also a good idea to equip your dog with a Sherley's Insecticidal Collar or Dogband beforehand—it could save you the trouble of getting rid of the odd flea on his return.

When you return, try not to blame the kennels if your dog has lost weight, or has lost his voice. Very few kennel owners would be likely to keep a dog short of food, but many dogs will fret and refuse to eat, and others will bark until they are hoarse, when they find themselves suddenly left in a strange place.

If your dog is really unhappy in kennels, try to make an arrangement with a dog owning friend to look after each other's dogs at holiday time—or better still take your dog with you if possible.

Bad Habits And How To Deal With Them

neuroses

Some of the bad habits of the dog may be generally classified as a return to primitive behaviour. After all, the wild dog needed to chase and kill game, but this is not acceptable in a civilised world. Other behaviour problems seem to relate more to human neuroses; for instance, dogs who suddenly become frightened of traffic, or terrified of being left alone in a room. Presumably something happened to disturb them, which they connect with a particular place, but it is very difficult for us to understand, or deal with the situation. It is worth remembering that the dog is by nature a pack animal and in the absence of a pack leader, he appreciates firm guidance from his owner as a substitute.

If you have brought your dog up from a pup, by the time he is fully grown he should be a reasonably well trained companion. However, if you take over the care of an adult dog, you may have some difficult behaviour problems to deal with. Some of these can be overcome by kind and sensible treatment, but others if they are of long standing may prove impossible to eradicate.

temperament

As the various breeds of dogs become more inbred, in the pursuit of show appearance, they seem to become worse in temperament. It is getting increasingly difficult to point to any one breed and say that it is 100% reliable. Even cocker spaniels, which were once a most placid breed are now often nervous and snappy, and the golden or red strains seem to be the most highly strung of all.

Remember that if you get a large dog this problem is going to be intensified. It is possible to live with a savage pekinese, but a savage alsatian, or doberman is a different proposition. It is probably true to say that overall, bitches are less aggressive and make better pets than dogs.

While dogs may inherit a tendency to be placid or nervous, a great deal depends on their upbringing. If you are always kind, firm and above all consistent with your dog, you will get a good response. On the other hand if you are excitable and inclined to 'fly off the handle', do not be surprised if your dog behaves in the same way.

biting

Never tease your pup, or allow the children to do so and never encourage your pup to growl or bite even in fun. It may seem amusing in a little pup, but it is much less so in an adult dog.

It is sad to say that a dog which has once bitten its owners will almost certainly do so again. In these circumstances you should pause and think very seriously as to whether this is a risk that you are prepared to take, particularly if there are children in the house. A dog which is really vicious should be painlessly destroyed. It is neither kind nor fair to give it to someone else.

postmen

Biting a postman has, regrettably, always been considered something of a joke, but obviously it is no joke to the postman. Unfortunately, many dogs who are trained to bark and guard the house, take a great dislike to some of the routine callers and especially those in uniform. It is worth taking time to introduce your dog to these people, if they are dog lovers, so that your dog accepts that they are welcome visitors; or if this proves impossible, to make sure that the dog is not left to roam unsupervised in the garden.

fighting

It may sound something of a contradiction, but it is often the more nervous and timid dogs which become fighters. It seems that they feel that attack is the best form of defence. An over-protective attitude on the part of the owner usually makes this situation worse. If you rush to pick up your dog as soon as another dog approaches, it gives the impression that there is something to fear. Try to exercise your dog right from the start in company with a friend's dog, so that he becomes less apprehensive of his own kind.

If your dog shows a tendency to attack other dogs while on the lead he must be checked. Stand still while the other dog walks past. Speak very sternly to your dog if he growls, or if necessary smack him with a rolled newspaper. As his behaviour improves, still make him stop, or sit while other dogs go past and then pat him and say 'good dog'.

sheep chasing

This must count as the worst vice that a dog can have and it is a serious worry for those who live in the country. A dog which is seen chasing sheep, or even seen in suspicious circumstances, may be shot by the farmer, and for this reason country dogs, just as much as those that live in the town, should never be allowed to wander on their own. The law that allows farmers this right may sound harsh, but terrible damage is inflicted on sheep and lambs each year by wandering or straying dogs. When training your dog, take every opportunity to walk it on the lead through fields where there are sheep and cattle. If the dog shows the slightest interest say 'No' in a very stern voice. If he makes any attempt to chase check him at once, and if necessary give a really hard smack. If this lesson is not learned it could some day cost your dog his life.

Chasing

cars and bicycles

This, though it is less common than some other bad habits, can be an equally difficult problem. Some dogs seem to be really maddened by the sound of an engine and something stronger than them comes over them and they are of course quite deaf to all your calls. If caught early, the habit may be checked by exercising the dog on the lead in traffic, and making it sit and wait calmly as each car goes by. However, if the habit has become really ingrained the only measure you can take is to see that the dog is never allowed to get out on its own. He could be the cause of a serious accident.

cats

Chasing cats should never be encouraged, even as a game. A dog can easily kill a kitten which has not learned to realise the danger, or a dog may be badly scratched by an older cat. Dogs and cats can live very happily in the same household when they get used to each other, and there is quite enough strife in this world without our encouraging it.

Destructiveness

chewing

This problem has already been discussed as it affects younger dogs. Most pups will chew up the occasional shoe if they get the chance, but if an older dog continues to destroy furniture or doors or wallpaper we must look further for the reason.

This sort of behaviour is most common in dogs which have had to change homes or have lacked a secure and reassuring start in life.

Make sure that the dog is getting as much exercise as possible—a tired dog is much less likely to be a destructive one. Concentrate on making the dog stay in his own bed, while you are in the room, so that he understands that this is where he is expected to stay. Use Sherley's Stop Chew on his favourite spots.

toys

Give him some strong toy of his own to chew if he wants, and of course confine him to one room where you have put everything possible out of reach. Sometimes leaving the radio on when you go out will provide a little reassurance. This can be a very difficult and expensive time in a dog owner's life, but don't despair—it won't last for ever.

false pregnancy

Bitches will sometimes show symptoms of false pregnancy about 8 or 9 weeks after a season. In this state they really imagine that they have puppies, and start to scratch up their blankets to make a bed for the imaginary offspring. So if you come home one day to find your normally well-behaved bitch has chewed up her blankets, this may be the reason.

Copraphagia

Young dogs will sometimes develop the very unpleasant habit of eating their own droppings—usually to the great dismay of their owners. It has been suggested that this indicates a dietary deficiency, but there is no conclusive evidence. If you are satisfied that your dog is in good physical condition there is no need to worry too much. The problem can usually be dealt with by taking simple practical measures. Never leave your dog alone in the garden or yard, and see that all droppings are cleared away, and disinfectant put down at once. Sprinkling pepper, or other unpleasant substances does not seem to deter dogs from this particular habit at all. When exercising, keep your dog on a lead, or at least until he has passed a motion, and you have got him well away from the place. Once again this really is something that they will grow out of.

Dog Shows And Kennel Club Regulations

Dog shows in England have been held since 1859, starting with a very simple show for pointers and setters. Today showing dogs has become immensely popular, and shows are held all over the country for the many different breeds, culminating each year with Crufts Dog Show in London. Here the top dogs of all varieties are seen, and dog breeders, and dog lovers from all over the world attend. The Kennel Club which holds the register of all pedigree dogs was formed in 1873, and since that time has done a great deal to promote concern for dogs, and their welfare.

Unfortunately it was not realised that the rather intensive inbreeding of dogs to produce their attractive show points was also leading to the appearance of some very unwelcome inherited faults. Among these we can include the condition known as hip dysplasia in alsatians, and the enlarged soft palate of some of the short-nosed breeds such as pugs, which makes it difficult for them to breath. Nowadays responsible breeders are trying to see that health and soundness of the dog is the first consideration, and it may be said that overall the showing of dogs has done much more good than harm.

Only registered pedigree dogs may be exhibited at shows organised under Kennel Club rules, but if you own a cross-breed pup you may often find a show in your district, where prizes are given for appearance, obedience, or charm.

Registering Your Pup

A pedigree dog is one whose dam and sire were both entered in the Kennel Club register. If your new puppy is a thoroughbred the breeder will supply you with a written pedigree. You can then apply to register your pup, by writing to the Kennel Club at their headquarters at 1, Clarges Street, Piccadilly, London W.1. Since by now a great number of dogs have been registered you will be required to give a choice of several names that you would like, and there is of course a small charge.

Preparing Your Dog For Show

If your dog is to be shown, he must of course be in tiptop condition. In the breeds where trimming is required, there is a case for getting expert advice from a breeder. It is a good idea to buy a book about your particular breed to learn all you can about the subject, and to get a good picture in your own mind of the show points, and the appearance of a good specimen of the breed.

When you are choosing a pup with a view to showing, check to see that it is free from any obvious faults such as over or under shot jaw, or kinks in the tail. If you are very inexperienced take an expert friend with you, or ask to buy the pup subject to a satisfactory examination by a veterinary surgeon. It can be very disappointing to pay a high price for a pup, only to find that it is of no use for showing.

All dogs should be vaccinated against distemper, and this is of special importance if you are attending shows, as at any place where a lot of dogs are gathered together the risk of infection is high. At all shows run under Kennel Club Rules a veterinary surgeon examines each dog, before it is admitted, and if he suspects that there is any infection, which might be passed on to other animals, the dog will be refused entry.

While showing your dog can be a pleasant hobby, if you mean to take it seriously, and if you have the good fortune to have picked a good dog, it can take up a lot of time, and involve a certain amount of expense. Breed shows are held all over the country and if your dog is to become a champion it is necessary to attend the appropriate shows to meet the competition.

Chapter 5
INTERNAL AND
EXTERNAL PARASITES
OF THE DOG

Internal Parasites

worms

Of all the subjects which cause anxiety to owners concerning their dogs' health, worms can be placed at the top of the list. Over the years a great deal of superstition and mythology has built up regarding the supposed symptoms caused by worms and the weird and horrific folk remedies which were used to get rid of them. There is really no need for this excessive alarm. Firstly, worms do not cause a great number of the conditions which are attributed to them and secondly, with modern drugs they can be quite safely eliminated without causing any distress to the patient.

roundworms and tapeworms

As far as is known most dogs, at some time in their lives, have worms. Usually this is during their puppyhood, and at this time the owner should always be on guard and look for symptoms. However, remember that a dog that appears quite healthy can pass, or vomit, worms and likewise there are many cases where the dog shows vague symptoms of ill-health which can be caused by worms.

The worms found in dogs in Britain fall into two main categories, roundworms and tapeworms. They are not blood-sucking worms, but live on the partly digested food material in the stomach and intestine. Unless they are present in very large quantities they are unlikely to produce symptoms of illness, except in the case of young puppies. If you see definite signs of worms, you should, both for the dog's sake and in the interest of hygiene, take measures to get rid of them. However, if your dog becomes ill, never assume that worms are the cause and commence treatment without consulting a veterinary surgeon.

Roundworms (Toxocara Canis)

Roundworms, also called ascarids, are mainly of importance in young pups and in pregnant bitches. They are only infrequently seen in dogs of two years or over.

recognition

In appearance they are round-bodied, rather similar to a thin earth worm; they can be up to 9″ in length but are usually much smaller,

55

and are of a whitish colour or pinkish brown due to ingested material.

how they spread The life cycle of the roundworm is quite simple; they are spread directly from dog to dog. The eggs, which are microscopic in size, and invisible to the naked eye, are passed in the faeces. They are ingested again by licking, and when swallowed develop in the intestines of the dog into larvae or microscopic immature worms. These then migrate through the blood stream to the lungs. They are then coughed up and swallowed again.

These larvae grow to maturity in the stomach and intestines and commence to produce eggs and repeat the cycle. The adult worms are usually noticed at this time when they are vomited, or passed in the faeces. In the grown dog the larvae tend to remain harmlessly encysted in the muscle, but in the female they become active again in pregnancy, with the result that puppies become infected through the blood stream before birth.

need to dose more than once It can be appreciated by an understanding of this life cycle that, as only adult worms in the intestine are destroyed by worm treatments further dosing has to be carried out at intervals, as new larvae hatch out, to ensure that all the worms are removed.

what to look for The symptoms can vary from quite serious to very mild. In young pups worms may cause abdominal distention and pain, loss of weight, vomiting or diarrhoea, and even rupture of the bowel. At post-mortem examination the stomach and intestines of these pups may be found to contain hundreds of worms. The migrating larvae in the lungs may also cause coughing, which can be an important symptom: these larvae may also travel through the liver, brain or other tissues.

routine dosing of pregnant bitch It is because of this risk to young pups that the routine dosing of the pregnant bitch is of so much importance. At this time the larvae will pass to the foetuses in the uterus if the bitch is pregnant. In this way the puppies will have fully developed mature worms in their intestines 4-5 weeks after they are born—this can be the most serious type of roundworm infestation.

treatment Modern treatment for roundworms does not necessitate starving the dog, and usually causes no distress at all. The remedies are palatable and easy to administer, and generally are very effective. Bitches should be treated in the week before and after whelping. Puppies may be treated from 3 weeks of age, and the treatment repeated at weekly or fortnightly intervals. Remember that re-infection can easily occur.

what wormer to use There are many products available to treat roundworms. The Sherley's range is listed in Chapter 8.

danger to children Although the roundworm cannot complete its life circle in humans, ingested eggs can cause serious conditions in children. They hatch into larvae in the gut and then migrate to various organs of the body, including the liver, lungs, eyes and brain, where they become permanently encysted. It is therefore of the greatest importance to see that puppies which are in contact with children are kept free from worms, and that a good standard of hygiene is maintained. The dog's excreta should be cleared away as soon as possible from gardens or exercise runs to prevent the ground becoming heavily contaminated with worm eggs, which can lay dormant in the topsoil for three or more years. Likewise, dogs should be discouraged from fouling public places where children play.

Tapeworms (Taenia and Dipylidium species)

Tapeworms are most commonly found in the adult dog. It always has to be remembered that tapeworms have to have an intermediate host, therefore successful treatment includes elimination of the intermediate host as well as removing the adult worms from the dog.

recognition

The so-called worm actually consists of a number of whitish coloured segments which are joined together to form the tape, terminating at the narrow end in a head which is attached by minute hooks to the lining of the stomach or intestine of the dog. They may be up to several feet long, but it is more often the individual segments (containing the eggs) which are seen as they are shed. These may appear as white wriggling particles, in the faeces, or around the anus (when they are often mistakenly described by owners as roundworms), or as dried-up cucumber-seed-like structures attached to the hair in the tail region.

how they spread

Tapeworms are never transmitted directly from dog to dog, but always through an intermediate host. These may include birds, mice, rabbits and lice, but the most common one for town dogs is the dog flea. The dog may swallow the flea containing the larvae of the tapeworm, while grooming, or may be infected while hunting rabbits etc., or eating fallen carcasses. The larva grows into a tapeworm and attaches itself to the intestine of the dog where it remains until it is mature and commences to shed segments containing the microscopic eggs, which are then eaten by the intermediate host to repeat the cycle.

what to look for

Except in the case of massive infestations, digestive symptoms do not occur. Tapeworms do not usually cause loss of weight, and fat dogs as well as thin ones may be heavily infested. The dog may show signs of anal irritation as a result of shedding segments.

control of intermediate host

Treatment should be carried out both for the sake of the dog, and for aesthetic and hygienic reasons. If re-infestation is to be avoided measures must be taken to get rid of the intermediate host. In the case of fleas and lice this involves regular dusting or bathing with a suitable insecticide, such as Vamoose or Sherley's Insecticidal Shampoo, especially in the summer months, or the wearing of a Sherley's Insecticidal Collar or Dogband.

For those dogs that are inveterate hunters and rely on other intermediate hosts to keep up their tapeworm infestation, the only answer is regular dosing with tapeworm remedies.

treatment

Tapeworms may sometimes prove rather difficult to eliminate, as unless the head, or scolex, is destroyed the worm will soon start to

57

grow again, even though a considerable part of the tape has been shed. If segments start to appear immediately after dosing it suggests that the treatment has not been fully effective and should be repeated, taking care to use a preparation that is designed specifically for tapeworm. If segments appear after a few weeks it is more likely that re-infestation has taken place and you should ensure that you are also dealing with the intermediate host of the tapeworm at the same time as you repeat the treatment.

what wormer to use

Sherley's Tapeworm treatments are listed in Chapter 8.

danger to humans

Dog tapeworms are only very rarely transmitted to humans. However infestation with echinococcus, a less common species, can very occasionally occur, and may be serious.

Hookworms (Uncinaria)

other worm parasites

These are much less commonly seen in Britain, but they are blood-sucking worms and cause serious loss of condition. They are susceptible to treatment with the drugs which are used for round-worm, but if in any doubt consult a veterinary surgeon.

Whipworms (Trichuris)

This is a rather rare type of worm infestation which would be diagnosed by a veterinary surgeon since they are not visible to the naked eye.

External Parasites

fleas, lice and ticks

Even under present day conditions, dogs are liable to become infected with the common ectoparasites, that is to say the parasites which live in, or on the skin. You may feel that because your house is kept spotlessly clean this is unlikely to happen, but any dog which is taken out for exercise is liable to pick up fleas, lice or less commonly ticks, and suffer accordingly.

Make a point of giving your dog a thorough grooming several times a week, and keep a careful watch for these parasites, especially in the summer months when they are most prevalent.

prevention

It may be wise to carry out prophylactic treatment with Vamoose anti-parasitic dusting powder or Sherley's Insecticidal Shampoo occasionally. There are also now available the Sherley's flea collars which provide more lasting protection where re-infestation is a problem. See the Sherley's range of anti-parasitic products in Chapter 8.

All bedding should be washed regularly with Sherley's Concentrated Disinfectant, and the box or basket scrubbed out, as it is here, in the case of fleas that the eggs are found. Fleas are unfortunately extremely resistant and can persist in carpets and upholstery for many weeks, without needing to feed. It seems that some dogs, like some people, are much more attractive to these insects and you may find that where two dogs are kept together, one will be constantly attacked by fleas or lice, while the other remains free.

58

The first sign of parasitic infestation that you will notice is persistent scratching, and loss of hair. If you fail to take action on this you may then be confronted with open sores, where the dog has bitten or scratched itself raw as a result of the intense irritation.

Fortunately there is little risk of transmission to humans. Dog lice never attack people; dog fleas will occasionally, and ticks only very infrequently, usually in moorland districts.

The Dog Flea

The common dog flea (ctenocephalides canis) is extremely active and prevalent in the summer and autumn months. In winter they tend to retreat into warm crevices in buildings, or into upholstery. It should be remembered that the flea is one of the intermediate hosts of the tapeworm and for this reason also it is important that dogs should be kept free.

Fleas are blackish brown, shiny and roughly 1/16th" in size. They tend to run very rapidly, rather than to jump and are sometimes quite difficult to detect. They may sometimes be found in clusters on the abdomen, or at the base of the tail. They are blood-sucking insects, and their very characteristic black, ash-like, excreta can very readily be seen on the dog's coat, or on the bedding. The eggs are laid on the bedding where they hatch out to form the immature larvae, which in turn become adult fleas.

The dog will start to scratch and there may be loss of hair. Later bare places will develop, and there may be open sores especially at the base of the tail.

Treatment by the use of Vamoose anti-parasitic powders or a medicated bath is usually very effective. Blankets should be burned if possible and all boxes or baskets disinfected.

To prevent re-infection a Sherley's flea collar is very effective. This is a thin collar impregnated with an insecticide which gives continuous protection over a period of months and keeps the dog free from parasites. Care should be taken to see that these collars do not become wet, and they should be removed if there is any sign of irritation of the skin in the neck region. See the Sherley's range in Chapter 8.

Hedgehog Fleas— If at any time your dog finds a hedgehog in the garden he may come in with his ears or face covered with tiny black insects. These are hedgehog fleas, and while they may cause distress for a short time, they do not live on dogs. Treatment, using a flea powder, is very quickly effective.

The Common Dog Louse

Lice (also called trichodectes canis) are tiny, pinkish-white in colour, and rather spherical in shape. They are quite slow-moving and attach themselves to the dog's skin, where they feed. They may be found all over the body, but more especially in the hair of the

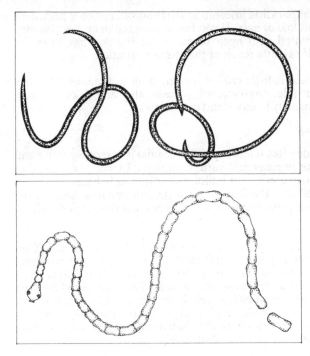

Roundworms.

Tapeworm showing the head on the left.

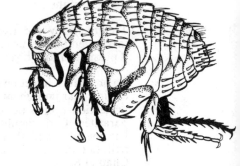

Dog flea.

Dog louse.   *Common tick.*

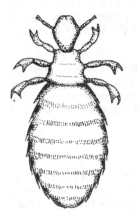
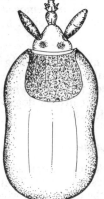

ears, particularly of the long-eared breeds. The eggs, or nits as they are called, have very much the appearance of scurf. However, if they are examined under a magnifying glass it will be seen that they are oval and shiny, and that each one is firmly attached to an individual hair. Lice can also be intermediate hosts for the tapeworm.

symptoms

Persistent scratching, loss of hair and sore places, especially on the flaps of the ears.

In very young pups severe pediculosis or infestation with lice, can lead to anaemia and even death.

treatment

Vamoose dusting powders and Sherley's Insecticidal Shampoo are effective, but the treatment should be repeated at weekly intervals to destroy the new lice as they hatch from the eggs. Since the eggs of lice are laid on the hair of the dog, there is less risk of contamination of bedding, but care should still be taken. With long-haired dogs it may be necessary to clip the hair, especially on the ears. If infected wounds are present it may be wise to consult a veterinary surgeon.

Sherley's flea collars are also effective against lice, and are the best method of preventing re-infestation.

Ticks

recognition

Ticks (ixodes and other species) are bluish black and bean-like in appearance. Their size varies, but they may be up to $\frac{1}{2}''$ in diameter when engorged with blood. At this stage they are sometimes mistaken for skin cyst. Examination under a magnifying glass will show the presence of legs, and a biting mouthpiece, by which the tick is attached to the dog.

Ticks are found mainly on moors, and in country districts where they are normally parasitic on sheep, but they will attach themselves to a dog, or less commonly to a person if the opportunity occurs.

Ticks are also found on hedgehogs, and this is sometimes the source of infestation in town dogs.

treatment

Where individual ticks are found they may usually be removed with tweezers, after applying a piece of cotton wool soaked in surgical spirit or Sherley's Antiseptic Lotion, taking care not to leave in place the biting 'head', or an abscess may form. Ticks will drop off on their own accord after a few days, when they have finished feeding. If there is a heavy infestation of ticks, a bath with a suitable additive is necessary, for instance Sherley's Insecticidal Shampoo. A Sherley's Dogband will quickly clear ticks.

Harvest Mites

These are harvest bugs, which cause considerable annoyance to humans as well as dogs in the country during the late summer. They are actually a kind of mite which burrows into the layers of skin, and in dogs they are found most frequently in the skin between the toes.

They are just visible to the naked eye, and groups of them have a red or yellowish appearance.

Treatment with Sherley's Insecticidal Shampoo produces a quick improvement.

Cheyletiella Parasitavorax

This is a less common mite, which is caught through contact with wild rabbits.

It is often difficult to recognise; there is irritation and usually a very thick white scurf forms, mainly along the back of the infected animal.

Treatment in the form of Vamoose anti-parasitic powders and Sherley's Insecticidal Shampoo should be given.

The Ear Mite

This mite (otodectes cynotis) is of considerable importance to the dog owner, as it lives only in the ear canal of dogs (and cats) where it causes great irritation. The dog reacts to this by shaking the head and scratching, causing exudation, and sometimes haemorrhage and thus pre-disposing to many of the intractable and chronic ear conditions which are seen. Cats, while they are very susceptible to ear mites, appear to be less sensitive to them. The condition in cats and especially in young kittens, is sometimes not suspected until a dog living in the house picks up the infection, and immediately shows his discomfort.

recognition

Ear mites are just visible to the naked eye, as pin point greyish dots, and they are easily visible under a magnifying glass. The main symptom is persistent shaking or scratching of the ears. On examination the ears are often found to be full of dry, dark brown wax.

treatment

If the diagnosis is certain, relief can quickly be obtained by the application of ear drops designed to destroy the mite. This should be repeated at weekly intervals, to catch the new mites as they emerge from the eggs. See Sherley's Canker Lotion and Powder in Chapter 8.

If the condition has persisted for sometime, bacterial infection is almost certain to have taken place, and veterinary advice should be sought.

grass seeds

A sudden onset of head shaking, especially after a walk through long grass may indicate the presence of grass seed in the ear, rather than an ear mite infection, and in this case also veterinary help will be needed.

mange and ringworm

There are three other important external parasites which can affect the dog; these are not visible to the naked eye, and they can only be definitely diagnosed by microscopic examination of a scraping of skin from the affected animal. They comprise of two types of mange, and ringworm, and they are of special interest because in the case of two of them there is considerable risk of transmission to man, particularly where dogs are allowed to sleep on chairs or beds.

Sarcoptic Mange

This is the most common type of mange, and it is caused by the mite sarcoptes scabiei. This mite burrows into the superficial layers of the dog's skin, where it lives and lays its eggs, causing intense irritation to its host. It is most common in puppies and young dogs, and it may become a serious problem in kennels if proper hygienic measures are not taken to control it.

recognition

In the early stages, sarcoptic mange is characterised by persistent scratching, followed as a result of this, by the appearance of reddish patches of inflammation in the axilla (arm pits) and on the insides of the thighs. There are often bare places around the eyes and scaly thickening of the ear flaps. The condition, if not checked, may spread all over the body of the dog, with the formation of scabs, sores, and bare places throughout the coat. There may be a general loss of condition as a result of the constant irritation.

Diagnosis may be confirmed by a veterinary surgeon who will examine a skin scraping, taken from one of the affected places, under a microscope.

transmission

Sarcoptic mange is readily transmissible, both to other dogs, and to people when it is known as scabies. Children are especially susceptible, probably because of their more delicate skin, and the fact that they are more likely to come in close contact with their pets while playing.

In humans the first signs of infection are usually red, irritable patches on the fingers, or wrists. If you have any reason to suspect infection, consult your doctor as soon as possible.

treatment

The application of a mange dressing like Sherley's Eczema and Mange Lotion or Sherley's Skin Cure, alternating with the use of Sherley's Insecticidal Shampoo will usually produce a good result and a marked lessening of irritation. Care must be taken to see that the dressing comes into contact with the affected areas. It may, in some cases, be helpful to clip the dog's hair, especially with long-coated breeds.

The dog should not be allowed to come into contact with other animals. The bedding should be boiled each week, and the basket or box, as well as all collars or harness, thoroughly scrubbed with Sherley's Concentrated Disinfectant.

The owner should remember the importance of washing the hands each time after handling or dressing the dog. Any swabs or cotton wool used for applying skin dressing should be disposed of by burning, if possible.

Finally remember that because the mange mites live in the layers of the skin it is hard to be certain when they have been totally eliminated. It is necessary therefore to persevere with treatment and hygienic measures for some time after the external symptoms have disappeared, or you may be disappointed by a recurrence of the problem.

Demodectic Or Follicular Mange

This type of mange is caused by demodex canis, a rather cigar-shaped mite which is just visible under a magnifying glass, and easily recognisable under a microscope. This mite lives in the deeper layers of the skin, coming to the skin surface only intermittently in its life cycle, and it also invades the lymphatic system and the glands of the affected dog. It will be understood therefore that it is a much more difficult condition to treat effectively.

recognition

Initially the appearance of dry scaly places in the dog's coat may be seen. Short-coated varieties, and in particular, dachshunds, seem to be most often affected and the dog may have a rather characteristic 'musty' or 'mousy' odour. The bare places may remain quiescent for sometime, but usually, as a result of scratching, bacterial infection follows, often with the presence of very resistant staphylococci and formation of small discharging pastules, or abscesses. The dog's skin tends to become thickened and wrinkled especially on the limbs, and if the condition is not checked it may lead to a severe illness, or even death, as a result of a generalised bacterial infection or septicaemia.

diagnosis

Diagnosis may be confirmed, as with sarcoptic mange, by a skin scraping, but it is sometimes less easy to demonstrate the presence of mites, because of their tendency to invade the deeper tissues of the dog's skin.

transmission

Demodectic mange is not transmissible to humans, and not readily transmissible between adult dogs. Transmission is thought to take place only from mother to pups in the very early stages of life. The pups may show signs of infection at once, but sometimes the mites may remain dormant in the tissues without giving any visible signs of their presence. This explains the sudden appearance of the lesions of demodectic mange in a dog which has obviously not been in contact with a case.

It is wiser not to breed from bitches which have had demodectic mange.

Where veterinary help is not available, treatment, in mild cases, may be attempted using the measures advised for sarcoptic mange. However, if there is bacterial infection it is important to consult a veterinary surgeon as soon as possible. Demodectic mange is extremely resistant, and difficult to treat, but with the use of modern antibiotics and other drugs it is usually possible to produce a great improvement, if not always a complete cure.

Ringworm

recognition

The **extremely contagious** skin condition known as ringworm is actually caused by a fungus (the most common type affecting the dog is called microsporon canis), which invades the individual hairs, causing them to break, or to die and fall out.

The lesions caused by ringworm are rather variable, and it is for this reason difficult to diagnose with certainty or to distinguish from other skin conditions. Typical ringworm is seen as circular lesions, usually rather pink and inflamed, with raised crusty edges. However, there may be simply irregular, smooth, bare places anywhere on the dog's coat. Irritation may sometimes, but not always, be present. The hairs at the edges of the bare places tend to be stubby and broken, and pull out easily.

transmission

It cannot be too strongly stressed that ringworm is extremely contagious, not only to other animals, but to humans, and especially children. Medical advice should be sought at once if there is any suspicion that anyone in the family may be affected.

The condition in dogs may be caught from calves, mice and rats, and also sometimes from other dogs, and cats (or from humans). In the case of infection from mice or rats the bare places may appear first on the muzzle.

Dogs in the country may be infected from contact with gates, or fences, where calves have been scratching. The spores of ringworm can remain alive on woodwork, furniture, or upholstery for several years.

diagnosis

Diagnosis should be carried out by a veterinary surgeon. He may examine the dog under a Wood's glass (an ultra violet light which causes the ringworm to glow, or fluoresce, in the dark), or examine a skin scraping taken from the dog under a microscope.

treatment

If you suspect ringworm always consult your veterinary surgeon, never attempt treatment on your own. Modern methods of treatment, including a very effective oral drug (a tablet) now make the condition much easier to control. However, remember that it is important that you persevere in carrying out the measures that your veterinary surgeon advises. The disappearance of the symptoms does not necessarily mean that you have got rid of the ringworm. Great care should be taken over disinfection, and bedding, basket and collars are better burned. A failure to observe these precautions may lead to a flare-up of infection even after many months.

Chapter 6
TREATMENT AND
FIRST AID IN ILLNESS

If you care for your dog it is important to learn to recognise the early stages of illness. Treatment given promptly is much more likely to be effective, and delay in getting proper advice does not give your veterinary surgeon a fair chance to help you. An observant, thoughtful owner will soon observe the small differences in behaviour indicating the onset of an illness that an outsider would miss.

Early Symptoms Of Illness

The most common symptoms of illness in the dog are listlessness, that is to say a reluctance to leave the basket, or go for a walk, and loss of appetite (known as anorexia).

is he ill? or not?

If your dog is reluctant to leave his bed it may be that he is suffering from a generalised illness, or that he is suffering from pain or injury to a limb which actually prevents him from getting up. It sometimes happens that a dog which has suffered some minor injury or strain which was not noticed during exercise, will stiffen up while lying in his basket, and find himself almost unable to get up on the following day. Taking a tit-bit of some kind to his basket will usually help to differentiate between these two kinds of trouble. An ill dog will usually refuse food, but one with some localised injury (unless he is in great pain) will usually eat.

Hot Or Cold Nose

It has always been considered that a dog with a hot nose was ill, but this is not necessarily the case. A normal dog, and especially a puppy, will very often have a warm dry nose when it wakes up from a sleep. Equally a dog with a cold wet nose may sometimes be found to be running a temperature. However, a runny nose, especially if there is a thick discharge, may well be a danger sign. Dogs do not suffer

a runny nose

from common colds in the human sense and a runny nose might indicate the onset of distemper.

Examining Your Dog

It is important in the case of suspected illness or injury, to be able to examine your dog thoroughly. A little applied common sense should tell you whether the problem is a minor ailment or injury, which you could attend to yourself, or whether you should get in touch with your veterinary surgeon or Animal Welfare Clinic for advice. Unless your dog is a real heavy-weight you will probably find it helpful to stand him on a low table under a good light to make a proper examination.

restraint

If some painful area, such as an injured nail or foot is to be examined, even the best mannered dogs may snap. The best method of restraint is to use a muzzle, and it is better to apply it from the start, rather than to wait until the dog has become upset and difficult, or you have been bitten.

muzzles

It is possible to buy a leather muzzle if you wish, to fit most sizes of dogs, but it is quite easy to improvise a satisfactory substitute, using

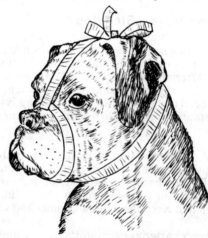

Tape muzzle for a short-nosed dog.

Tape muzzle for a long-nosed dog.

a length of strong bandage. A loop of bandage is slipped over the dog's nose, crossed under the jaw, then tied firmly behind the ears (see diagrams). The pressure of the muzzle rests on the bones of the dog's nose, and does not restrict its breathing, but quite effectively prevents biting.

sedation

If you have a dog which is really unmanageable your veterinary surgeon may be willing to give you a tranquillizing tablet to administer before taking the patient to the surgery for an examination.

Examination For Wounds

Wounds in the dog are often obscured by hair, especially in the more shaggy members of the species. If you suspect that your dog might have an injury, first clip the hair away carefully, using a pair of blunt-ended scissors if possible and then bathe, using Sherley's Antiseptic Lotion. Small cuts are often found in the pads and in the web of the foot as a result of broken glass. If the wound is very small, it may be sufficient to bathe it well and then keep it covered with a bandage or clean sock for a day or two. If the wound looks large enough to require stitching, or if it appears infected or if there is a lot of bleeding, always get professional advice.

Haemmorhage — Bleeding

Haemmorhage may be of two kinds. The most common is venous (as the result of damage to a vein). In this, while there may be quite a lot of blood, it is darkish in colour, and the bleeding is fairly easy to control. Arterial haemmorhage is less common, because arteries are stronger, but it is much more serious. Bright red blood spurts from the damaged blood vessel and the bleeding is very difficult to stop. It is important to get in touch with a veterinary surgeon as soon as possible.

first aid

The best method to stop bleeding is to apply a pressure bandage. Put plenty of cotton wool over the bleeding point, and bandage firmly. Do not bathe the wound, or remove the bandage even if blood starts to show through (see illustrations of bandage applications). Keep the patient as quiet and warm as possible.

applying a tourniquet

In very severe arterial haemmorhage in a limb it may sometimes be necessary to apply a tourniquet to stop the bleeding. A tourniquet can be improvised, using a strong clean handkerchief. Apply the handkerchief as a tight bandage above the point of bleeding (nearer to the head), and tie the two ends. If this is insufficient to check the bleeding, slip a pencil into a layer of the bandage, and twist to exert greater pressure.

Warning—A tourniquet must never be left on continuously for longer than 10 minutes. It will cut off all blood supply to the limb and gangrene will be caused which may well result in the death of the patient.

Fractures — Broken Limbs

It is not always easy to tell if a limb is broken and an X-ray may be necessary, but if the leg hangs limply and the animal is unable to support any weight, a fracture should be suspected and help obtained as soon as possible. Try to keep the dog as still as possible. It is a help to transport the patient in its own basket or bed.

Compound Fracture—This is the term applied to a fracture in which there is also an open wound.

Greenstick Fracture—This term is used to describe what happens in the bones of young animals. The bones are softer and tend to bend rather than to shatter as they do in an older animal.

Taking The Temperature

normal temperature

In the dog the temperature is taken by inserting a thermometer (moistened with a little petroleum jelly) for about 2″ into the rectum. It is wise to get someone to help you with this job, as thermometers are very easily broken if the patient struggles, and they are quite expensive to replace. A veterinary thermometer is a useful aid. This is rather heavier than the human variety, has a blunt end, and is easier to read. Normal temperature in the dog is about 101.5°F. The temperature may be raised after exercise, but in a listless dog a rise of more than 1° probably indicates the onset of illness. A depressed temperature is found normally in a bitch just before whelping, but it also occurs as a result of shock, or collapse, when it is a very serious indication of ill health.

Taking The Pulse

It is possible to detect the pulse in the femoral artery, which runs on the inner side and at the top of the hind leg, but there may be considerable variations (62-130/minute), and it is rather the quality of the pulse beat (which can be detected by an experienced person) than the rate, which gives an indication of the dog's state of health.

Symptoms To Look For

anorexia or loss of appetite

If a dog is generally fussy about its food, it is probably an indication that you are overfeeding it, but if a normally hungry dog refuses its food, it may well be a sign of illness. However, it is as well to check that he or she has not had the chance to get at a rubbish bin, or some left-over bones, before starting to worry seriously, and to make sure that there is no physical reason interfering with eating, such as a piece of stick or bone lodged in a tooth.

cough

A cough may be a symptom of some general illness, such as canine distemper, or kennel cough, or tonsilitis, but it can also sometimes indicate an obstruction, such as a bone in the throat. In elderly dogs a cough is often heard as a result of heart trouble, particularly after exertion. Coughing in young puppies can be due to roundworm infestation; the larvae, during their life cycle, migrate through the chest, before developing in the stomach into adult worms (see chapter 5 on Internal Parasites). Because of the extreme seriousness of distemper in young puppies it is always wiser to treat a cough as being a possible symptom of illness, and to consult a veterinary surgeon rather than to attempt treatment on your own. It must be emphasised again that dogs do not get coughs and colds as a result of the common cold virus of humans, and they cannot catch or transmit human colds.

diarrhoea and constipation

These two conditions can easily be confused. If you notice that your dog is straining, apparently trying to pass a motion, this may be due to the presence of hard faeces in the bowel, as a result, often, of eating bones, but it may also be due to the fact that he has passed a liquid motion, and now is straining hard, but only getting rid of a little mucus, or blood. Never administer a laxative without being completely certain which condition you are treating. If a laxative is to be given it should always be a mild one like Sherley's Lik-A-Med. Harsh laxatives such as castor oil are rarely given now. They cause abdominal pain, and the immediate laxative effect is often followed by secondary constipation. Liver, while it is an excellent food for dogs, may sometimes cause diarrhoea, so it is wise to check on the contents of any tinned foods which are fed.

passing blood

Dogs will quite often pass blood, following severe diarrhoea, but it is a symptom which should be taken seriously and it is best always to consult a veterinary surgeon.

first aid for diarrhoea

It is best to cut out food completely for 24 hours and give only small drinks of glucose and water (one teaspoonful of glucose dissolved in one cup of water). If the condition improves, give a light diet, such as arrowroot milk puddings, or steamed fish, with a little brown bread, for a day or two. If the diarrhoea does not improve, always consult a veterinary surgeon, as it can soon lead to considerable loss of condition. Straining is usually caused by some discomfort in the bowel, but it may also result from inability to pass urine, as a result of some obstruction in the bladder, or to pain in the bladder as a result of cystitis. In middle-aged male dogs straining may indicate an enlarged prostate gland, and in the pregnant bitch it may signal the start of whelping.

vomiting

Dogs seem to have a natural tendency to regurgitate their food, and it is not uncommon for a healthy dog which has eaten his meal too quickly, to bring it back almost unchanged—and to immediately eat it again. It is probable that in the wild state this easy regurgitation may have been a safety measure when a dog had eaten something unwise, which might otherwise have harmed him.

persistent vomiting

If vomiting is persistent this is a much more worrying symptom and must be taken seriously. It can be one of the early signs of a number of illnesses, ranging from gastro-enteritis, to kidney disease and jaundice, or pyometra (see Chapter 7) in the bitch. It may also be an indicator that the dog has picked up an irritant poison put down for mice and rats, or that it has swallowed a foreign body, that is to say some object which cannot be digested and will soon set up an obstruction, with symptoms of serious illness. In the case of puppies this may be something like a child's toy, which it has picked up from the floor, but with older dogs it is most often a chop or chicken bone, or a stone which has been swallowed while playing.

vomiting blood

This often follows persistent vomiting, as a result of a ruptured blood vessel in the stomach. It is a potentially serious symptom, and it is wise to consult a veterinary surgeon, as soon as possible.

Starvation is always the best immediate policy if there is vomiting, and it is best to withold both food and water at first. A dog which has vomited repeatedly often develops a voracious thirst, and if it is allowed access to plain cold water it will continue a cycle of drinking and vomiting until it becomes completely dehydrated and exhausted. While waiting to consult a veterinary surgeon, it is best to give only small drinks (about one tablespoonful every hour) of either soda water, or glucose and water (in the proportions of one teaspoon of glucose to one teacup of water).

Pain

It is not always easy to tell from simple observation if a dog is suffering pain. A limp is usually a sign of pain in the limb, but may equally result from shortening of the limb following a healed fracture. A dog with a slipped disc syndrome will cry out with pain, but one with a serious abdominal condition will as a rule stand with its back hunched and look wretched. Dogs cannot tell us how they feel, so it is really important that the owner who is in any doubt should consult a veterinary surgeon.

General Care Of The Sick Dog

If your dog is under treatment by a veterinary surgeon it is important to carry out all the instructions you are given. Tablets or medicines should always be given at the correct times, but if you are unable to give them, or feel that they are not suiting your dog, always ring up for advice, rather than waiting until your next appointment, and leaving the dog without medication meanwhile.

warmth
and quiet

As a general rule a sick dog requires warmth and quiet. See that the basket or bed is in a peaceful corner, near a radiator, or give a well-wrapped hot water bottle to supply comfort. Unless advised otherwise in a particular case, fresh water should be freely available. Dogs can live for an amazingly long time on water alone.

foods

Lactol, or egg beaten in milk, is an excellent invalid food. Broth made from chicken or rabbit is usually very acceptable, and the many strained meat and fish preparations now available for babies are excellent for tempting a sick dog.

grooming

Dogs, like people, usually feel better when ill if they are clean and tidy, so don't give up your grooming routine. Your dog will quite appreciate a gentle brushing or combing, and any discharge from the eyes or nose should be carefully bathed or cleaned away. Blankets and bed covers should be regularly changed and washed.

Infectious Diseases

If your dog is suffering from an infectious disease it really is important to see that he is kept as far as possible completely isolated. This means exercising only in your own garden or yard, and it is better to discourage any dog-owning friends from coming to call, as infection can easily be carried on clothes or shoes.

After a contagious disease such as mange or ringworm, all bedding should be destroyed, not forgetting the collar and lead. After a case of distemper it is not safe to bring another dog (unless it is inoculated) into the house for several months.

Accidents

After a road accident it is often quite difficult to assess the amount of damage. A dog may sometimes be knocked unconscious and then quite suddenly recover, and be completely normal. Equally a dog which at first seems unhurt, may collapse later as a result of internal haemmorhage. It is best, while awaiting the opinion of the veterinary surgeon, to keep the dog as quiet and warm as possible. If at all possible get him inside, and if you suspect that there may be a broken limb try to improvise a stretcher, or carry him in his own box or basket to avoid any unnecessary movement.

Administration Of Medicines

Giving tablets and medicines to dogs often seems to present great problems to the owner. If the dog is still taking food, it is well worth trying persuasion. It is not advisable to put tablets in the food, as these are usually found, and the dog becomes very suspicious of its next meal. Much better to put the tablet, or halved tablet if it is a large one, into a piece of butter, cheese or meat, and give it separately as a treat—but give your dog credit for having some intelligence and carry out the disguising out of sight.

In the case where a dog is ill and off food, a more direct approach must be used.

tablets

If the tablets are likely to have an unpleasant taste it is better to put them in a small piece of cheese before giving them. Sit your dog down, preferably in a corner where he cannot back away, then open the mouth with a hand on the upper jaw, and with the other hand

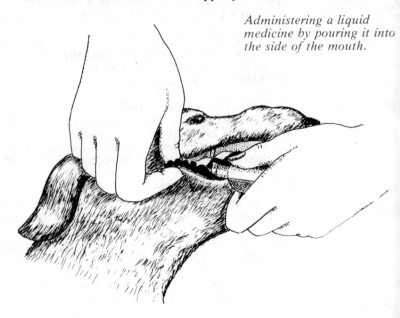

Administering a liquid medicine by pouring it into the side of the mouth.

push the tablet right to the back of the tongue, as far down as possible. Hold the mouth shut until you are sure that he has swallowed.

liquid medicines

These are really easier to give. If necessary a difficult tablet can usually be crushed to a powder, and mixed with a little milk to give as a liquid. In this case sit your dog down, tilt the head back slightly. then without opening the jaw, pull out the pouch of skin at the corner of the mouth, and pour the dose of medicine down. It will trickle between the teeth to the back of the mouth, and the dog will usually swallow quite readily. If you are on your own it is easier to measure the dose of medicine into a small bottle, rather than attempt to hold a spoon in a wobbly hand.

skin dressings

If any creams or dressings are to be applied to the dog's skin, it is well worth carrying out the job immediately before a walk. The subsequent distractions will serve to prevent the dog from sitting down and licking off all the dressing and ensure that external applications do not become internal ones.

injections

It may occasionally be necessary for an owner to administer drugs by hypodermic injection, under the supervision of a veterinary surgeon. In almost all cases today a disposable syringe will be used, and these arrive in a sterile pack and can be disposed of after use. The syringes are graduated in cubic centimetres, and great care must be taken to measure the correct dose. When withdrawing fluid from a sealed bottle, through the rubber cap, it is necessary to inject a quantity of air equivalent to the size of the injection into the bottle, or a vacuum will develop and it will become extremely difficult to withdraw the plunger of the syringe.

subcutaneous injections

The most usual method of injection is by the subcutaneous route, that is to say, simply under the skin, and this is the only type that an owner is likely to tackle unaided, but injections may also be given intramuscularly or intravenously. Having drawn the correct amount of the injection into the syringe, a small area of the skin should be swabbed with surgical spirit, or Sherley's Antiseptic Lotion. The ideal site for the injection is the loose skin over the scruff of the neck. Get a friend to hold the patient still, then having first ensured that there is no air in the syringe by expelling one drop of fluid from the needle, lift a fold of skin, and plunge the needle directly through the skin. Press down the plunger slowly and steadily to expel the fluid. After withdrawing the needle, again swab over the injection site with cotton wool and spirit. As a rule there is little or no bleeding, and there should be very little pain. With a skilled operator a dog will often show no sign of noticing the injection at all.

enemas

Enemas are used (generally under veterinary instruction) to treat cases of severe constipation. A solution of soapy water or glycerine and water is introduced into the rectum using a rubber enema syringe.

Bandaging Wounds

In the wild state it is true that the dog probably licked wounds, but there are many occasions when a bandage is necessary, to prevent haemmorhage, to prevent dirt getting into a wound, or to prevent a dog from opening up a wound that has been stitched.

legs and feet

Wounds affecting the limbs and feet are probably the most common ones that an owner encounters, and it is a great help to be able to apply a satisfactory bandage. In dealing with the foot it is best to pack wisps of cotton wool between the toes to avoid constriction of the pads. Even when the wound is higher up the limb it is wiser to include the foot in the bandage. A constricting bandage half way up a limb will have an effect rather like a tourniquet, and the lower half of the leg will start to swell.

Having thoroughly cleansed the wound, apply an antiseptic dusting powder or Sherley's Antiseptic Lotion, and cover with a piece of clean gauze. Next apply a layer of cotton wool all over the leg, to prevent constriction, and bandage with an even pressure, starting from the foot. Crepe bandages are particularly good for this purpose as the elasticity helps to grip the limb. Finally add a few bands of adhesive plaster strip to prevent the bandage slipping or being pulled off by the patient, and cover the whole leg with a man's stretch sock to keep the dressing clean.

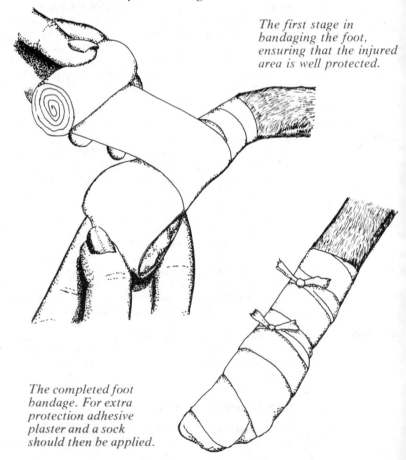

The first stage in bandaging the foot, ensuring that the injured area is well protected.

The completed foot bandage. For extra protection adhesive plaster and a sock should then be applied.

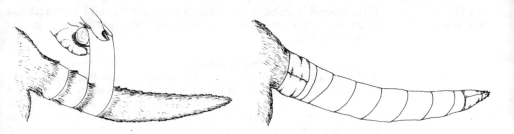

When bandaging the tail, include hair in each turn of the first layer to prevent slippage.

The tail bandage should be finished with adhesive plaster that extends onto uncovered hair.

tails

Tails are especially difficult to bandage satisfactorily, because the dressings can so easily be wagged, or pulled off. Start with gauze and a layer of cotton wool, as with the foot, but when bandaging, take care to fold back groups of hairs, and include them in the bandage layers to prevent it from slipping off. Finish with bands of adhesive plaster which extend beyond the bandage onto the hair of the tail.

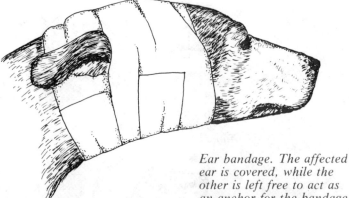

Ear bandage. The affected ear is covered, while the other is left free to act as an anchor for the bandage.

ears

Ears are very susceptible to injury, as a result of fights, or barbed wire, and they tend to bleed very profusely. The situation is worsened by the dog's natural tendency to shake its head, so it is essential that the ear is immobilised by a firm bandage. At the same time care must be taken to avoid constriction of the throat, so this is another case where a crepe bandage is helpful.

Apply a fairly generous pad of cotton wool to the ear, and in the case of long-eared breeds, fold the ear back over the top of the head. Apply the bandage around the head, leaving the unaffected ear free, as a peg, or anchor, to prevent the bandage slipping back. Finish with strips of adhesive plaster, and finally make a Balaclava helmet out of the leg and welt of a man's sock (leaving a hole for the free ear), to protect the dressing, and keep it clean.

body wounds

Body wounds can be quite difficult to deal with, and bandages are often necessary to protect surgical wounds, particularly in the abdominal area.

A "many-tailed bandage", that is to say a broad strip of old sheet, with ties all the way along, to tie on top of the back, is usually effective in covering an abdominal wound. If two holes are made to take the front legs, it will prevent the bandage from slipping back. (see diagram). Alternatively a child's sweater, with the dog's front legs going through the armholes, will make an effective cover for most of the body. A clean piece of gauze can be stitched inside the jacket to cover the affected area.

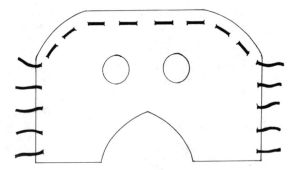

A body bandage suitable for covering abdominal wounds.

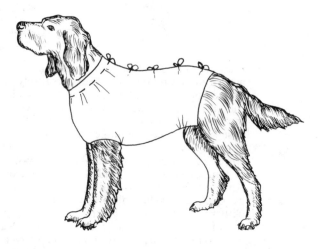

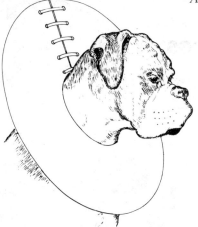

A simple Elizabethan collar.

Elizabethan collar

This usually consists of a funnel of strong cardboard, which is attached to the dog's collar, and projects forward beyond the muzzle. It is an effective way of preventing a dog from rubbing at injuries on the head, and it will also prevent it from biting at the feet or body, in cases of irritation.

Euthanasia

The sad time comes inevitably when we have to decide to end the life of a much-loved pet. This is always a very difficult decision to make, and it is only too easy for a devoted owner to keep a pet alive longer than is really kind. If you genuinely feel that your dog, as a result of illness, or old age and infirmity, is unable to enjoy its life, it is much better to face facts and make a decision. The break will have to come soon, and you may well reproach yourself if you have allowed your pet to suffer for a few unnecessary days, or weeks. Equally there are occasions when a dog has to be destroyed because it is unmanageable, or vicious. It is the owner's duty to see that it is painlessly destroyed, rather than to pass it on, with all its problems, to someone else.

injection

Euthanasia by pentobarbitone injection is by far the best and most humane method. Your veterinary surgeon can supply you with a strong tranquillizing tablet, which will save the dog from being frightened or alarmed by being taken to the surgery or clinic. He will then be given an injection (usually intravenously) which will induce deep anaesthesia, followed by death, without any pain at all.

electrical

Electrical euthanaters are widely used, and if they are really efficient they cause instant death. However, doubts have been expressed as to whether they are completely humane in effect, and it is better that the dog should be given a sedative before being put in the euthanasia cabinet.

humane killers

If properly used, humane killers are instant in effect, and they are sometimes necessary in an emergency situation, but it is not a thing that most owners would be happy to watch.

Chapter 7
DISEASES AND AILMENTS OF DOGS

This chapter is intended to help the owner to recognise or understand some of the more common ailments of the dog, but it is not intended to be a manual of home treatment. It is important to remember that since your dog cannot talk, it is only too easy for the owner to be mistaken when diagnosing a complaint, and in this way the dog may, quite unintentionally, be caused unnecessary suffering. In all areas there are veterinary surgeons available for consultation, and in most districts there are welfare clinics, for those who are unable to pay fees, so if you suspect that your pet is ill, don't delay, but consult expert advice at once.

Abscess

An abscess is usually seen as a raised, painful swelling, due to the formation of pus under the skin, and they may occur anywhere. The swelling will as a rule gradually increase in size and become tense, until it bursts to discharge pus and blood. There may be a rise in temperature and the dog will feel ill, and may resent handling.

Abscesses often form as a result of dog, or rat bites, or from the presence of grass awns in the feet or limbs.

Anal Gland Abscess—See Anal Glands

Tooth Abscess—The most common tooth abscess is the malar abscess, which develops as a result of infection at the root of the large carnassial molar tooth.

The symptoms are the development of a swelling on the dog's cheek, just below the eye. The swelling eventually bursts, but continues to fill up and reform. The condition will not heal until the affected tooth has been removed, so consult your veterinary surgeon.

First Aid Treatment—For a superficial abscess, the best treatment is to bathe with warm water and antiseptic solution (Sherley's Antiseptic Lotion is suitable) until the abscess bursts. Continue to bathe the wound to keep it open and prevent healing taking place too quickly, or another abscess will soon appear on the same site. In all except very minor cases, antibiotic treatment will be necessary, so consult your veterinary surgeon.

Allergy — Nettlerash — Urticaria

Nettlerash is the body reaction of a particular dog (or person) to a food, or other substance. It can best be understood by considering the fact that while many people eat shellfish without the slightest ill effect, in a few people it causes a rash or other symptoms. In the dog it is often extremely difficult to be certain what has produced the symptoms, but a reaction to a wasp or bee sting is a common cause.

Symptoms—It is usually noticed that quite suddenly the dog is covered with raised blotches. In smooth-haired breeds the skin over the head area may present an almost quilted appearance, and swelling of the gums or throat may cause the dog some discomfort.

Treatment—In many cases the symptoms disappear spontaneously, after a few hours, but they may return again. Consult your veterinary surgeon. Antihistamine treatment will usually give quick relief from the symptoms.

Anal Glands

These are enclosed in two pear-shaped sacs, situated under the skin at each side of the anus, in both dogs and bitches. They are scent glands and produce a very foul smelling secretion, which is normally discharged through a tiny, pore-like opening at each side of the rectum. They are of no use to the civilised dog and may sometimes be removed surgically if necessary. In the wild state the glands probably emptied as a result of the pressure of hard bulky material in the bowel, but with modern soft foods the glands may fail to empty and cause the dog considerable irritation and discomfort. A dog with anal gland troubles will very typically slide along the ground on its bottom, or lick and bite continually under its tail. This condition is often confused with worm infestation and it is important to be certain of the cause before carrying out treatment.

Treatment—The anal gland can be expressed (or emptied) quite easily by a veterinary surgeon and this is something that the owner can learn to do, if shown. Infected anal glands may continue to produce an excessive evil smelling and sometimes blood stained discharge. Antibiotic treatment is usually needed.

Anal Gland Abscess—In this case the duct becomes blocked, and the anal sac fills up with septic material. A red swelling is seen at one side of the tail and the dog is usually in considerable pain. Consult a veterinary surgeon as soon as possible.

Anal Prolapse—This is seen most commonly in young pups, and results from excessive straining, usually following an attack of diarrhoea. A portion of the bowel is extruded from the rectum, and it quickly becomes red, swollen and painful. In some cases the bowel may become telescoped upon itself, and this is known as an intususseption.

First Aid—It may be possible to return the prolapse, having first lubricated it with liquid paraffin, but in most cases the dog will immediately start to strain. Consult a veterinary surgeon as soon as possible.

Arthritis And Rheumatism

These two conditions can be rather difficult to differentiate. Acute rheumatism is sometimes seen in working dogs, after some unusual exercise, as for instance with gun dogs at the beginning of the shooting season, and it is characterised by muscular stiffness. It can usually be relieved by a pain-killing tablet, such as Sherley's Rheumatine Tablets.

Arthritis affects the joints, more often of older dogs, and as with the same condition in humans, there is no certain cure, although modern drugs can provide a great deal of improvement.

Bad Breath

This is a condition which causes great worry to dog owners, but as a rule, with common sense it can be dealt with. In nearly all cases bad breath is due to either bad teeth, tartar on the teeth, or gum infection as a result of these conditions. Get your veterinary surgeon to remove any teeth that are decayed. Your dog will be happier and healthier without them; then keep the teeth white by regularly cleaning with peroxide, or tooth powder (see Chapter 4). Amplex Veterinary Tablets can help control bad breath and other body odours, particularly when due to the type of food eaten.

A piece of bone lodged in a tooth can cause soreness, and resulting foul breath, but this of course, is soon dealt with. In older dogs bad breath can indicate uraemia, as a result of kindney failure. This is a serious condition, but it will be accompanied by other signs of illness. In dogs of the spaniel type, so-called bad breath is often due to an infection in the loose folds of the cheek, as a result of dribbling—consult your veterinary surgeon.

Balanitis

This is an infection of the sheath of the penis, which is quite common, especially in young dogs, and can be considered as more unpleasant than serious. There is usually a copious thick, whitish discharge, and the dog will tend to lick, and clean himself a great deal. Swabbing with a solution of hydrogen peroxide will often help, but in a persistent case, consult your veterinary surgeon.

Baldness—Alopecia

Elderly dogs, especially poodles, do sometimes suffer from genuine baldness, and as with humans, the prospects of improvement are poor. However, if the loss of hair is accompanied by soreness, or scratching, it may indicate a skin infection (see Skin Diseases).

Bites

Bites from other dogs, or from rats, are a common cause of wounds and abscesses in dogs. If you know that your dog has been bitten, immediately clip the hair away from the area, and bathe with an antiseptic solution such as Sherley's Antiseptic Lotion. Prompt treatment can do much to prevent the development of bacterial infection. However, if the bite has become septic it is important to consult a veterinary surgeon as antibiotic treatment may be necessary.

Snake bites may occur in moorland areas. If you suspect that your dog has been bitten by a snake, keep him quiet and warm and consult a veterinary surgeon as soon as possible.

Bladder Troubles

Cystitis, or inflammation of the bladder, occurs more often in bitches than dogs. The affected animal will strain frequently, passing only small amounts of urine, often blood-stained and often with a strong smell of ammonia. This is a painful condition and it is important to get veterinary advice as soon as possible.

Bladder Stones—Stones may form in the bladder, kidneys or urethra of dogs and bitches, as a result of the deposition of mineral salts. The symptoms are very similar to those of cystitis, but are more serious and there may be a complete inability to pass water. Consult a veterinary surgeon as soon as possible. An operation may be necessary, but if the condition is caught in time there is a good chance of recovery. Unfortunately in dogs which form bladder stones there is a tendency for the condition to recur.

Bleeding

The most common sites of bleeding in the dog are the feet, ears and tail (see Chapter 6). Some dogs, usually the smooth coated varieties, may develop chronic bleeding of the ear tips or tail, as a result of shaking the head, or knocking the tail. This is a difficult condition to cure, and it is best to consult a veterinary surgeon.

Bronchitis

Bronchitis is usually characterised by a cough, or noisy breathing. It may occur on its own, or as a complication of distemper, or with a heart condition in older animals. While chronic bronchitis can be alleviated by drugs, it cannot be completely cured as a rule.

Bruises

Dogs do suffer from bruises, though they are usually only noticed if they occur on the hairless areas (see Haematomas).

Burns And Scalds

Many dogs develop scorching, or even burns in the winter months, as a result of sitting too close to an electric fire. Moral—always use a fire guard. Scalds are only too common as a result of upset kettles or saucepans, and they tend to be serious, because the dog's coat holds the heat.

First Aid—Immediately soak the area in cold water, and if the dog will allow it, trim away the hair. The amount of damage may not be obvious at first, but after a few days, blisters may appear, and result in a very severe open wound. With bad scalds the hair may never grow again on the affected places. Keep the dog quiet and warm, as there may be shock, and contact a veterinary surgeon as soon as possible.

Cancer – See Tumours

Canker

This is an old-fashioned name, which applies to all ear troubles in the dog. See Otitis.

Castration

Castration is the name given to the neutering of male dogs. The operation is generally carried out at about 6 months old for choice, though it can be at any age. The advantages are that dogs are usually less aggressive after the operation, and are certainly less likely to stray in search of bitches. The disadvantage is that they are more likely to put on weight, if care is not taken over their feeding and exercise.

Car Sickness — See Chapter 4, Caring For Your Dog.

Catarrh

Catarrh is seen most commonly as a symptom of distemper, but it can also occur as a result of infection in the sinuses, as a result of a foreign body such as a grass awn in the nose, or due to the presence of tumours in the nasal passages. The symptoms are sneezing, or a persistent discharge from the nose. Unfortunately the condition can be extremely difficult to treat, and it is best to consult a veterinary surgeon.

Choking

Choking may often happen as a result of swallowing a bone. If your dog is coughing and you suspect that he may have an obstruction, carry out the following test: push a small ball of soft bread down the dog's throat, as if administering a tablet. If there is any obstruction the bread will be returned within about a minute, and you should consult a veterinary surgeon as soon as possible. It is dangerous to throw any ball of small size for a dog to catch as these have been known to stick in the gullet and cause suffocation.

Chorea

This is seen as a result of the affect of the distemper virus on the nervous system. A muscle, or a group of muscles or even a whole limb will be subject to a nervous twitch which is present all the time, and is often more noticeable when the dog is asleep. The symptoms of chorea will sometimes appear after an attack of distemper which was so slight as to pass unnoticed. If the twitch is confined to a small area it may be possible for the dog to live a fairly normal life, but if the condition is progressive it will probably lead to paralysis, and it may be kinder to have the dog humanely destroyed.

Collapse

Collapse may be due to a number of conditions and must be dealt with accordingly. Short-nosed dogs such as pekes, bulldogs and pugs sometimes collapse from heat stroke in summer. In this condition the breathing may be very distressed, the tongue will be a very dark bluish colour and the dog may become unconscious. This condition is very serious so while contacting a veterinary surgeon get the patient into a cool draught, pull out the tongue to avoid choking, and if possible apply ice packs.

Heart attacks and fits (see Fits) may also be causes of collapse, and it is not always easy to distinguish between the two. Keep the patient quiet and warm while consulting a veterinary surgeon. In many cases the duration of the collapse is brief, and the dog may appear better before you are able to get help, but it is wise to get advice on future treatment.

In collapse as a result of a stroke (usually in older animals) the animal will usually remain dazed and unsteady for a considerable time. If the eyes are examined they will usually show a characteristic flickering from side to side.

Don't despair if your dog is unconscious as a result of a road accident. As with humans, the results are very unpredictable, and the dog could make a complete recovery.

It is not unusual to see dogs, and especially young pups, in a state of collapse, as a result of eating sleeping tablets. Remember that young dogs will eat absolutely anything and see that all tranquillizers and other tablets are kept safely out of reach (see Poisons).

Cryptorchidism And Monorchidism

In this condition in dogs, either one or both testicles are retained, either in the abdomen, or under the skin of the inguinal region. These animals are able to breed, but it is not advisable to use them at stud, as the conditions seem to be hereditary. In later life there is a tendency for the misplaced testicle to become abnormally enlarged and an operation may be necessary.

Cysts

These are basically swellings in the body which contain a fluid, or semi-fluid secretion. They are as a rule less painful than an abscess, unless complicated by infection.

Sebaceous cysts occur very often on the skin of some varieties of dogs, especially pekes. If large enough to cause discomfort it is best to consult a veterinary surgeon.

A salivary cyst appears as a large soft swelling at one side of the jaw and usually requires surgery. A ranula is a salivary cyst under the tongue.

Cysts are sometimes seen in the third eyelid of young dogs, and although they look alarming, usually respond well to a simple operation.

Ovarian cysts are due to the formation of a vesicle containing fluid on an ovary, usually causing symptoms of irregular heats or difficulties in breeding. Hormone treatment is sometimes effective but surgery may be necessary.

Inter-digital cysts (cysts between the toes) cause a great deal of trouble to some dogs and their owners too (see Chapter 4).

They occur most commonly in dogs where the feet have rather deep 'wells' between the pads where mud and dirt can accumulate. Particles of grit penetrate the skin and either form sterile cysts, filled with fluid, or if there is bacterial infection, painful abscesses between the toes. Care of the feet can do much to avoid these troubles (see Chapter 4). The hair around and under the feet should be kept short, and the feet should always be well washed after exercise in muddy weather.

Treatment—Bathing the foot with Sherley's Antiseptic Lotion will usually give relief, and in many cases the cyst will burst, and subside after about 48 hours. If the cyst is infected, antibiotic treatment or surgery may be needed, so consult your veterinary surgeon.

Deafness

Some all-white dogs (especially bull terriers) suffer from a hereditary form of deafness, and unfortunately there is no cure for this. Deafness as a result of wax in the ears seems less common in dogs than in humans, but deafness as a result of old age degenerations in the internal ear is quite usual. It is not unkind to keep a deaf animal, but extra care must be taken to avoid danger in traffic. The most noticeable fact about a deaf dog is that if asleep, it fails to react as a normal dog would when anyone enters the room.

Diabetes

Diabetes is seen most commonly in bitches of middle age, but it can occur in dogs or bitches of all ages. The symptoms are of severe thirst, usually accompanied by a good appetite in the early stages, and considerable loss of weight. It is due to a failure in the metabolism of sugar in the body.

Diabetes mellitus can be demonstrated by the presence of sugar in the urine, but in diabetes insipidus there is no sugar in the urine, and diagnosis is less easy, and it may easily be confused with other conditions.

Diabetes mellitus can be treated by dieting, and the administration of insulin, but a great deal will depend on the owner's ability as a nurse in carrying out the veterinary surgeon's advice, as the treatment must be continued throughout life.

Diarrhoea

Diarrhoea may occur as a symptom in a great many conditions (see Chapter 6). If you think it may be the result of simple over-indulgence, or unusual food, starvation is the best treatment. Give no solid food at all for 24 hours, and only small drinks of glucose and water (one teaspoon to one cup of water). If this checks the diarrhoea, return gradually to a normal diet, but if there is no improvement in 24 hours, consult a veterinary surgeon. Sherley's Anti-diarrhoea Tablets may be of value in mild cases.

Dislocations

A dislocation is the name given to the accidental displacement of two bones at a normal joint. A very common dislocation is that of the toe joint in greyhounds, or of the hip joint in young dogs, when characteristically one leg will be seen to be shorter than the other. It is often difficult to differentiate a dislocation from a fracture and an X-ray may be necessary, so consult a veterinary surgeon as soon as possible. Many dislocations can be reduced, or returned to normal by manipulating (under a general anaesthetic), but in some cases it is necessary to immobilise the limb, with a splint or a plaster cast. In a few cases the dislocation may prove very difficult to reduce or may constantly re-dislocate, in which case further corrective measures may be necessary.

Distemper Or The Canine Distemper Complex

This name covers all types of distemper in dogs, including hard pad. This highly fatal virus disease of dogs is made even more serious by the fact that those patients which do recover are so often left with debilitating nervous after-effects. The virulence of the disease can vary greatly in different outbreaks (rather as in human influenza), and in the early stages it can be quite difficult to detect.

Hard pad is a type of distemper, characterised particularly by severe nervous symptoms. First reported soon after the end of World War II, it was so called because, sometimes in the later stages of the disease the skin becomes thickened and hard, especially over the pads. It is worth noting that dry or hard pads, or lameness on their own are most unlikely to indicate the presence of hard pad virus, as this is one of the last symptoms to be seen in the disease.

Incubation Period—Symptoms of distemper usually start within 14 days of contact with an infected animal.

Symptoms—The symptoms of distemper are very variable, and unfortunately, are easy to miss in the early stages. The dog is usually listless and may not want food and if the temperature is checked it will be found to be above normal. These symptoms may improve, only to recur again after a few days. Next, characteristically the eyes become inflamed and there is usually a discharge from the eyes and nose. The dog will sneeze and cough and may develop pneumonia as a result of secondary bacterial infection.

Bowel symptoms—There is often a very persistent diarrhoea and in the later stages the dog may lose control of its bowel movements.

Nervous Symptoms—At about 6-8 weeks after the onset of the disease, and often when the other symptoms seem at last to be improving, nervous symptoms may commence. These may start as a twitch in an isolated group of muscles (see Chorea) or as fits, or as a gradual paralysis, shown at first by a trailing of the hind legs. In the great majority of cases these symptoms become progressively worse. The dog may go into continuous fits, gradually become completely paralysed and lose all control over bladder and bowels. Distressingly at this stage, though the dog may be unable to stand or recognise its owner, it will often eat voraciously if food is put in front of it. From this stage recovery is very rare indeed, and the conscientious owner must consider whether euthanasia is the kindest course.

Prevention—Nowadays it can almost be said that dogs need not get distemper, as the preventative vaccination is more than 95% effective. Consult your own veterinary surgeon or local Animal Welfare Clinic about the correct age for vaccination (usually from about 9 weeks old) and remember that it is essential to see that your pup does not come in contact with infection before he is vaccinated. This means that he must be kept either in the house, or in a totally enclosed yard or garden, as distemper virus is extremely infectious and contagious and can easily be picked up either from the roads, or even from people's clothes,-without direct contact with an infected dog.

Booster injections are needed to maintain your pet's immunity at a satisfactory level, so consult your veterinary surgeon about the appropriate time.

Treatment—If you suspect that your dog has distemper, contact a veterinary surgeon as soon as possible. Try to avoid taking your dog into the waiting room without previous warning, or you may unthinkingly pass on the disease to other pets. There is no treatment which is effective against the distemper virus itself, but modern drugs can do much to relieve the distressing symptoms of the disease.

Nursing—Good nursing can do a great deal to help in a distemper case. Try to provide nourishing and interesting foods. A dog with severe catarrhal symptoms will be unable to smell foods, and hence loses interest in eating. The eyes should be bathed frequently, and soothed with Sherley's Eye Lotion Capsules. The nose should be cleaned with damp cotton wool swabs, and Sherley's Veterinary Ointment applied to prevent cracking. Remember to destroy all dressings by burning to prevent the spread of infection. Dogs, like people, feel better if they are clean and tidy, so don't altogether give up the daily grooming. Even a very ill dog will often appreciate a gentle combing. Finally remember that tender loving care still plays a great part in recovery, even in the age of antibiotics and this is what you, as an owner, can supply.

Dropsy Or Ascites

This is an abnormal accumulation of fluid in a body cavity. A mild form of abdominal ascites is seen sometimes in young pups, as a result of malnutrition or roundworm infestation, giving a typically pot-bellied appearance.

In older dogs ascites is seen often as a result of poor heart function and in a mild case the condition can be improved by treatment with suitable drugs. Advanced cases, and those that are due to liver failure, or obstructive growths, have a very poor outlook. Abdominal ascites is not as a rule a painful condition, but if the fluid enters the chest, the animal will be in great distress, and it will be noticed that it seems afraid to lie down because of the difficulty in breathing.

Eclampsia Or Milk Fever

This very serious condition is seen in bitches which are feeding pups or very occasionally in late pregnancy, and is due to a deficiency of calcium in the blood stream (see Chapter 2).

Eczema And Dermatitis

These two names are usually applied to skin conditions for which there is no obvious infective agent. Skin infections due to external parasites are fully dealt with in Chapter 5. Having said this, it is still true that what we term an eczema may be due to the presence of just one or two fleas in a dog which is highly sensitive, or allergic to them. If your dog is scratching with no particular evidence as to the reason, it is always worth giving a thorough dusting with Vamoose first.

Nowadays skin irritations of unknown origin are an extremely difficult problem amongst dogs. It is thought that most of them are allergic in nature—that is to say that the dog is sensitive to some particular item in its surroundings, or in its food, but identifying the substance can be very difficult. Wool and detergents are some of the things which have been blamed, but to eliminate them from your dog's surroundings is almost impossible. Particular foods may not suit individual dogs, so it is worth excluding one food at a time from your dog's diet, for about a fortnight at a time, and seeing if this produces any improvement.

Before assuming that your dog's skin troubles are due to an allergy, have a good look at the state of his coat. If there are matts or tangles, or dead hair which needs thinning out, don't be surprised if he is itchy and uncomfortable. Finally, most dogs are more prone to skin troubles in warm weather. This may simply be as a result of the increased temperature, but as this period coincides with the time when external parasites are most common, we have come full circle and can probably say that the great proportion of dogs' skin troubles are due to parasites.

First Aid Measures—If your dog suddenly develops an acutely irritable, or sore and weeping lesion it is best to consult your veterinary surgeon. In the meantime it is usually safe to clip away the hair from the affected area, apply Sherley's Eczema and Mange Lotion every few hours with a pad of cotton wool and protect the area either with a loose covering, or by means of an Elizabethan collar, to prevent the dog from making the condition worse than it need be.

Encephalitis

This term is sometimes applied to the brain symptoms caused by the distemper virus (see Distemper).

Entropian

This is a congenital condition affecting the eyelids of dogs, especially chows and spaniels. Either the top or bottom eyelid, or both, are inturning, and as a consequence the lashes rub continually on the eyeball, causing irritation and weeping. This condition can be cured by a corrective operation so consult your veterinary surgeon.

Eye Conditions

The dog, unlike man, has a third eyelid, or nictitating membrane. This is a pinkish membrane situated in the inner corner of the eye, which is particularly obvious in bloodhounds and spaniels. This is a perfectly normal part of the dog's anatomy and serves as a protection in any painful condition of the eye. Many owners on seeing the third eyelid partly across the eye assume that the dog is going blind, but this is, of course, not true.

Conjunctivitis—This may result from an infection, or from a foreign body of some kind in the eye. As a first aid measure, bathe the eye gently with cool, boiled water or use Sherley's Eye Lotion Capsules, but consult a veterinary surgeon as soon as possible.

Blue Eye—An opacity of the surface of the eye can result from injury, or from the effect of a virus infection.

Eye Ulcers—These are actually injuries to the eye surface and they are common in dogs such as pekes which have bulging eyes. Consult your veterinary surgeon as soon as possible as these are not only very painful, but can lead to complete loss of sight in the affected eye. It is most important to prevent the dog from scratching at the eye and making the condition worse.

Glaucoma—This is a condition seen most often in older dogs in which there is increased fluid pressure in the eye. Consult a veterinary surgeon as treatment can improve this condition, which if left will result in blindness.

Cataract—This is an opacity, or clouding of the lens situated at the back of the dog's eye. In almost all older dogs a mild degree of cataract develops, and is seen as a bluish shadow at the back of the eye, or sometimes as a greenish gold reflection in the eye in an artificial light. In most cases the dog is still able to see, though less well, and there is no need for any treatment. In severe cataract the lens will appear chalky white, and the dog will be blind. Some cases will respond to surgery, but it is much less successful than in man because of the difficulty involved in keeping the dog still, and the wound sterile.

Blindness—If your dog loses his sight it may still be possible for him to enjoy his life with a little extra care from his owner. Much depends on individual circumstances, but it is worth considering all aspects before deciding to part with your pet. Dogs depend almost as much on their sense of sound and smell as on their sight.

Prolapsed Eyeball—In breeds such as pekes with protruding eyeballs the eyes sometimes come out of their sockets, as a result of accidents or fights. It is sometimes possible to replace the eye immediately, by lifting the loose skin above and below the eye, to allow the eye to fall back into its socket. If not, contact a veterinary surgeon as soon as possible, or the eye may be totally damaged and have to be removed.

Progressive Retinal Atrophy—Known as P.R.A., this is an inherited condition causing blindness in certain breeds, i.e. labradors.

Fish Hooks

Dogs in riverside areas quite frequently pick up fish hooks, all over their bodies, and suffer accordingly. Most fish hooks are barbed, so take great care in trying to remove them. If in difficulty consult your veterinary surgeon. He will be able to give a local, or general anaesthetic to make the job painless.

False Pregnancy

In the period usually about 6-9 weeks after the end of a season a bitch, although she has not been mated will often show all the signs and symptoms of pregnancy (see Chapter 2).

Fits

Fits may be divided into 3 groups:—

1. **Puppy Fits**—These are considered to be due to incorrect feeding, teething, or roundworm infestation. They are usually only transient in nature, but it is wiser to consult your veterinary surgeon. The puppy may seem over-excited or may fall on its side and froth at the mouth briefly. In a fit a dog may snap even at its owner, so it is wiser to leave it alone, in a quiet dark room to recover.

2. **Distemper Fits**—These are extremely serious (see Distemper).

3. **Epileptic Fits**—These are rarely seen in dogs of under 18 months old. The fits tend to occur at fairly regular intervals, from once a year to as often as once each week. They vary very much in their degree of seriousness, and once having started will almost always continue throughout life. A dog in an epileptic fit will usually froth at the mouth, the muscles may twitch involuntarily, and the dog will fall to the ground with the legs moving in a paddling action. It will often involuntarily empty its bladder and bowel. It may appear completely unconscious and unable to recognise anyone. The fit can last from a few seconds to 10 minutes or more and afterwards the dog will appear rather dazed and unsteady for a little while. Although this description sounds very distressing, tablets prescribed by your veterinary surgeon can do much to control epileptic fits and many owners find it quite possible to accept and live with the situation.

Flatulence

Many dogs suffer from flatulence or wind after eating some particular food such as liver and the symptoms can make them very disagreeable to live with for a while. The obvious answer is to alter the diet, and for immediate treatment, a teaspoonful of Milk of Magnesia or a Sherley's Gastrine Tablet sometimes help.

A more serious kind of flatulence is due to a torsion or twist of the stomach. The dog will be in considerable pain, the abdomen will be distended and the dog will stand very stiffly in one position. Contact a veterinary surgeon as soon as possible.

Fractures —See Chapter 6

These may be treated by splinting, or encasing in plaster of Paris to immobilise the limb. Today they are more often repaired by internal fixation, using a metal pin or plate.

Pelvic Fracture—This is difficult to treat, but in reasonably young dogs rest and careful nursing will often effect a cure.

Gastritis — Indigestion — Colic

Dogs, and especially young pups, often suffer a sudden attack of colic or stomach pain after bolting food. Food given directly from a refrigerator can produce a similar effect. Normally a little Milk of Magnesia, Sherley's Gastrine Tablets, or even a teaspoonful of brandy diluted in warm water, will give some relief.

Some dogs periodically vomit up a little bile, without apparently suffering from an illness. However, if stomach pain or sickness occurs frequently, it is wise to consult your veterinary surgeon, as it may be a symptom of illness.

Grass Seeds Or Barley Awns

These get into the eyes, ears and feet of dogs throughout the summer months. It is a wise precaution to go through your dog's coat if you have been for a walk in rough grassland and remove the culprits before they do harm.

Haematomas

Haematomas are really large blood blisters under the skin and can occur anywhere on the body as a result of a knock, but they are seen most often in the ear flaps of long eared dogs. They appear usually as an oval, fluctuating swelling under the skin and are uncomfortable, rather than acutely painful like an abscess. They are frequently self-inflicted, as a result of scratching at ears infected with ear mites. Small haematomas will eventually re-absorb and disappear, but larger ones usually require surgery. Remember to treat the ear condition as well or the condition may recur.

Heart Disease

In older dogs, heart disease is usually due to weakness in the heart valves, which are no longer able to maintain the blood circulation at its normal rate. The symptoms are a general slowing down, difficult breathing, sometimes with a cough on any exertion. In severe cases there may be ascites (see Dropsy). Treatment with drugs of the digitalis group can produce a considerable improvement in the symptoms and prolong life, so consult your veterinary surgeon.

Heart Failure

Heart failure can be extremely distressing to watch; the dog will collapse, the mouth and gums are whitish in colour, and the dog gasps for breath. See a veterinary surgeon as soon as possible.

Hernia

Hernias result from a weak place in the muscles, which allows the protrusion of abdominal organs, or abdominal fat under the skin, causing a soft fluctuating swelling. This may occur at any point on the abdomen as a result of accident, when they are more correctly termed a rupture, but the more usual sites are:

1. **Umbilical Hernia**—This is formed at birth from a failure of the abdominal wall to heal over completely at the umbilicus. A very small umbilical hernia may do no harm, but it is wiser to consult your veterinary surgeon in case an operation is necessary.

2. **Inguinal Hernia**—These may occur at either side of the lower abdomen in bitches. They should be repaired, because in pregnancy they form a potential risk when the extra weight of puppies can enlarge the hernia opening. Inguinal hernia is much less common in male dogs, when it is known as 'scrotal hernia' as the hernia contents, usually a loop of bowel, tend to descend into the scrotum.

3. **Diaphragmatic Hernia**—This may follow an accident. The partition between the abdomen and chest is damaged. The symptoms are usually distressed breathing and reluctance to lie down.

4. **Perineal Hernia**—This occurs most commonly in older male dogs, as a result of constant straining, from chronic constipation, or prostate gland enlargement. A soft swelling appears at one side of the anus, due to muscle breakdown and may gradually enlarge to form a circular area of swelling under the tail and around the anus. This is usually the most difficult hernia to correct, because of its situation, its cause and the age of the patient.

Hip Dysplasia

This is a condition which has been recognised in recent years, and is causing great anxiety to breeders of larger types of dogs such as alsatians and retrievers, as the condition is hereditary. The symptoms of the condition are at first lameness, and on X-ray examination it will be seen that the head of the femur (the long bone of the leg) is malformed, and will not fit into the socket in the pelvic bone. The condition is incurable and while it may be possible to keep the dog, its walk will never be completely normal, and in late life there may be paralysis. In some cases an operation to remove the head of the femur may be helpful.

Hiccough

Young pups sometimes suffer from hiccoughs—usually as a result of eating too quickly, eating the wrong foods, or roundworm infestation.

Hoarseness

Many dogs are hoarse, or without their bark upon return from kennels. Don't blame the kennels, but try to take your dog on holiday with you next time.

Hysteria —See Fits.

Incontinence

Incontinence of urine is sometimes seen in older dogs as a result of senile degeneration of the nerves and is unlikely to respond to any treatment.

In spayed bitches occasionally, incontinence will be seen. The bitch may wet her basket without appearing to notice. This is thought to be due to a hormone deficiency and usually responds well to hormone therapy. Consult your veterinary surgeon.

Young pups may wet through excitement or nervousness, but this form of incontinence improves with maturity.

Infectious Viral Hepatitis — Rubarth's Disease

This is a distemper-like infection, characterised by high temperatures and caused by a virus which attacks the liver. It sometimes causes a characteristic blue opacity of the eye. The disease can be prevented by the use of the 3-in-1 types of distemper vaccine.

Jaundice

This is a symptom, rather than a specific disease. The yellow colour, which indicates liver disfunction, is usually noticed first on the inner surface of the lower eye-lids. It then becomes visible on the bare parts of the skin and finally, in severe cases, colours the whole body including the whites of the eyes. It will be noticed that the urine is a very deep yellow, or brownish colour. The seriousness of jaundice depends on its cause and it is wise to contact your veterinary surgeon as soon as you notice symptoms.

1. **Mild Hepatitis**—With this, the dog will usually feel listless and off food for only a day or two, and the colour will fade quite quickly.

2. **Leptospiral Jaundice**—Weil's disease—This is an acute and very often fatal disease, which is transmitted by rats. It is characterised by a high temperature, vomiting, thirst, and a jaundiced colour. This disease can be prevented by the use of the 3-in-1 type of distemper vaccination which also protects against leptospiral kidney disease and virus hepatitis. Weil's disease can also affect man.

3. **Liver Tumours**—These are unfortunately rather common, usually in older dogs. The symptoms are very much like Weil's disease but are more gradual in onset. The outlook is very poor indeed.

First Aid Measures—Avoid any fatty foods and give only very small amounts of glucose and water to drink.

Kennel Cough Or Infectious Tracheitis

This is a persistent, infectious cough which occurs most commonly under kennel conditions. As a rule the dog does not seem ill and the condition recovers quite quickly. If any complications develop consult a veterinary surgeon.

Kidney Disease—Nephritis

This can be sub-divided into two categories 1) acute leptospiral kidney disease, usually in young dogs and 2) chronic kidney disease of older dogs.

Leptospiral kidney disease is characterised by a sudden high temperature, vomiting and loss of weight. If treated in time it usually responds well to antibiotics and it can be prevented by the 3-in-1 vaccination.

Chronic kidney disease may result from a leptospiral infection in youth, or may be associated with the degenerative processes of old age. The kidney is no longer working as an effective filter to eliminate waste products from the body and retain the valuable substances which it needs. The result of this is a kind of self-poisoning and the dog becomes thin, develops an excessive thirst and starts vomiting. It will usually pass large quantities of rather pale-coloured urine, which if examined will be found to contain abnormal amounts of protein (albumen). In the final stages the dog develops uraemia. It will vomit constantly and in spite of all this will continue to crave for water. The tongue becomes brownish in colour and the breath has a very typical foul smell. If this stage is reached euthanasia is the only humane solution.

Treatment—While kidney damage cannot be repaired, medicines and diet can do much to prolong life. Consult your veterinary surgeon if you suspect trouble.

Lameness

This is one of the most common complaints of dogs, and it almost always indicates pain in a limb, although very occasionally it may indicate a mechanical shortening of the limb, as a result of a previous injury. If your dog is lame, always examine the foot first for thorns etc, as this is by far the most common site of injury. Fractures, dislocations, sprains or strains or rheumatism may also be causes of lameness, so if you are unable to detect the cause always consult a veterinary surgeon.

Mastitis

This is inflammation of the milk glands and while it is usually seen in bitches which are feeding pups, it can occur even in young maiden bitches. The symptoms are redness and a painful swelling on a milk gland, and the bitch may be off food and run a temperature. Consult a veterinary surgeon as soon as possible.

Mammary Tumours

These are extremely common in bitches of middle age or older, and they should always be taken seriously. They may vary from a small hard pea-like nodule on a milk gland, to a large ulcerating swelling with abscess formation. They may always, potentially, be malignant (cancerous) in nature, and it is generally considered that early surgery gives the best chance of recovery. Consult your veterinary surgeon.

Mange —See Chapter 5 on External Parasites

Metritis

This is an abnormal discharge from the womb or uterus and the term is usually applied to an infection after whelping (see Chapter 2). There is usually a foul smelling discharge from the vulva, which may be blood-stained and the bitch will run a temperature. The condition is serious so consult a veterinary surgeon as soon as possible (See also Pyometra).

Milk Fever —See Eclampsia

This condition should not be confused with Mastitis.

Otitis (Canker)

This general term covers all inflammatory conditions affecting the ear canal of the dog. The two principal causes of ear troubles in the dog are the structure of the ear and the presence of parasites (ear mites). In addition to these you may also get foreign bodies in the ear such as grass awns, or sometimes tumours.

The shape of the deep ear canal in itself predisposes to trouble, as if there is any exudation, infected discharge tends to collect, rather than to drain away. In some breeds such as poodles, hair grows from within the ear canal, and if it is not regularly removed soon becomes matted, and together with accumulated wax, soon leads to a painful, or irritable ear. In all the flap-eared breeds (notably spaniels and poodles) the heavy ear

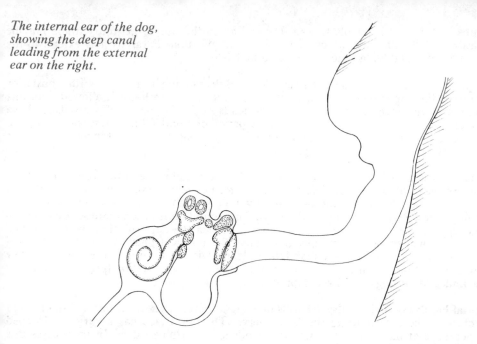

The internal ear of the dog, showing the deep canal leading from the external ear on the right.

flap prevents the free circulation of air around the ear, and produces a humid atmosphere ideal for the growth of bacteria.

Parasitic infection with the ear mite, otodectes (see Chapter 4) causes intense irritation. As a result the dog scratches and shakes the head, causing small injuries to the inner surface of the ear; bacterial infection follows and if treatment is not given promptly the result may be a very prolonged and intractable case of ear trouble.

Care of the ears can do much to avoid ear trouble (see Chapter 4).

Treatment—This will depend very much on the cause. In an uncomplicated case of parasitic otitis an immediate improvement will result from the application of a Sherley's canker treatment (see Chapter 5 External Parasites).

If bacterial infection has taken place the situation is more difficult. However, modern antibiotic and corticosteroid treatment can do much to help, so consult your veterinary surgeon.

In some cases an operation (an aural resection) may be needed to allow adequate drainage to the ear to help recovery.

Paralysis

Paralysis results from injury to a nerve. The most common type of paralysis seen in dogs is posterior paralysis which may result from an injury to the spine or as a sequel to a slipped disc or as a result of a distemper infection, when the degeneration of the nerves will continue, and the situation is almost without hope. The dogs most commonly affected are those with long backs, such as dachshunds. The dog will be found to be quite unable to support its weight on the back legs, and if stood up, will characteristically try to stand on the fronts of the bent-over feet. There is a loss of feeling in the hind limbs and the tail is unable to wag. Depending on the site of the injury, there may be paralysis of the bladder, which is a serious complication. Paralysis may extend to the fore part of the body, in which case the outlook is very grave.

Repair or regeneration of nerves is very slow and the nursing is difficult. With a posterior paralysis the dog is inclined to drag itself around by its fore limbs if allowed, and this combined with incontinence of urine soon leads to the formation of sores. Dogs have been known to make a recovery even after a period of months, but unless you are able to devote a very great deal of time to nursing your dog it may be kinder to consider euthanasia.

Radial Paralysis—This results from damage to the radial nerve in the fore limb, from a blow on the front of the shoulder, where the nerve lies near the surface. The dog will trail the limb loosely from the shoulder, and it will be found that there is a complete loss of feeling over a varying amount of the limb. This condition is much more serious than at first appears. Because there is no feeling in the leg the dog will allow it to drag and become damaged, and when bleeding starts the dog will gnaw at the foot, causing terrible injuries and gangrene may follow. It is advisable to protect the limb for a few days, to see if there is any improvement. If not, consider amputation (preferably high up the limb). Many dogs have lived happily for years with only three legs.

Facial Paralysis—Bell's palsy—This is much less commonly seen. It results usually from a blow on the face injuring the facial nerve. The dog's face has a curious, drooped appearance at one side, and there is a tendency to dribble saliva. In most cases this condition will gradually improve.

Pneumonia Or Inflammation Of The Lungs

This is seen most often as a complication of distemper, though it can occur on its own. The symptoms are a raised temperature, loss of appetite and distressed painful breathing. Treatment with antibiotics will usually produce a rapid improvement, so consult a veterinary surgeon as soon as possible. As with distemper, good nursing can do much to help.

Pleurisy—This is usually seen as a complication of pneumonia, and is in fact an exudation of infected fluid around the lungs. It is a serious and painful condition.

Poisoning

Every year many dogs are poisoned and it is almost invariably the fault of their owners. Dogs should not be allowed to wander and have the opportunity to rummage through other people's dustbins. Tablets prescribed for humans or dogs should be kept in a high cupboard (locked if there are children in the house). Medicines which are very helpful if taken correctly can be dangerous in overdose.

Rat or mouse poisons should never be put down in a house where there are pets. Even those labelled 'harmless to pets', may well be dangerous if taken in large amounts. Warfarin, for example, which is the most widely used rat poison, is extremely palatable to dogs and can cause fatal haemorrhages. For many of the modern weed killers there is no antidote, and if taken they are fatal to man as well as dogs.

Strychnine, a poison which causes terrible convulsions and death, is still sold to farmers to poison moles, in quantities sufficient to kill a family.

Treatment—If you know that your dog has swallowed a poison of some kind, immediately give it an emetic to make it vomit. The most useful everyday emetic substances are:

1. Washing soda (though this is less common today). A piece about the size of a hazelnut should be pushed down the dog's throat.

2. Strong salt and water solution, given like a dose of medicine. Then keep the dog warm and contact a veterinary surgeon, and tell him quite clearly what kind of poison you suspect.

Finally, if your dog is being sick don't automatically conclude that he has been maliciously poisoned. Search your conscience and remember if you gave him a mutton bone a few days before.

The Prostate Gland

This is a secondary sexual gland in the male dog. It is situated over the neck of the bladder and beneath the rectum. In the normal dog it is roughly the size of a marble, but as a result of enlargement, or tumour formation, usually in older dogs, it may reach the size of an orange, or even larger. Because of its situation there may be difficulty in passing faeces or urine and the dog often strains a great deal and shows signs of pain.

Treatment in cases of enlargement (hyperplasia) by administering female sex hormones, is usually very effective, but in some cases castration is advised to give more lasting results. In the case of a malignant growth the outlook is poor.

Pyometra

Pyometra is a very common condition affecting the uterus or womb of bitches, in the period up to 9 weeks after a season. It is most common in the middle-aged bitch, but it can occur even after the first season.

Symptoms—The bitch usually develops a very marked thirst, she may be listless and there is vomiting in the later stages. The temperature is raised and the bitch develops such a distended abdomen that the owner may suspect that she is having puppies. The reason for this distention is the accumulation of very foul-smelling pus in the uterus, and if no treatment is given, the bitch will either die of a ruptured uterus, or of toxaemia from absorbing the poison into her system.

Open Pyometra—In this case the cervix, or neck of the uterus, remains open, and the discharge is overflowing and draining away all the time. Usually the first symptom that an owner notices is that the bitch is constantly cleaning herself, as if she were still in season. There is usually a pronounced thirst, and although open prymetra is less sudden in onset, it is still almost invariably fatal if not treated.

Treatment—If your bitch is showing any of the symptoms mentioned consult a veterinary surgeon as soon as possible. Postponement of even a few days could cost your pet's life. In nearly all cases a hysterectomy operation is needed, together with antibiotic treatment. Do not delay visiting your veterinary surgeon through dread of an operation.

With modern methods of anaesthesia and tranquillizers your pet will suffer no pain or distress.

There is a mistaken idea that allowing a bitch to have a litter of pups will prevent her from developing pyometra. This is not the case. The only effective way of preventing this condition is by sterilising the bitch early in life.

Rabies

Rabies is a very serious disease of both dogs and man which is almost invariably fatal. It does not exist in Britain because of the very strict quarantine laws. The reason for the period of 6 months is that the infected dog may take this length of time to develop symptoms. If you ever feel tempted to try to smuggle a dog through customs, remember that you might be responsible for an outbreak of rabies that killed many pets and many people in a very dreadful way (see also Chapter 4).

Rabies Vaccination—This is now allowed in certain circumstances for dogs that are going abroad. Consult your veterinary surgeon.

Rabies is present in most countries of the world, notable exceptions apart from Britain, being Australia, New Zealand, Japan, Malta and Cyprus, but regardless of their origin, dogs (and other mammalian species) from anywhere abroad are required to observe 6 months quarantine on importation. The strict quarantine regulations have undoubtedly been the major factor in keeping the country free of this scourge which is almost invariably fatal to the animal or human victim. At the present time rabies is widespread in Europe where it has gained a firm hold since the end of the last war. With the red fox being mainly responsible for the spread of disease in the last few years, it has made serious inroads into North-east France with the likelihood that it will reach the Channel Coast before long. When rabies becomes established in wildlife it is very difficult if not impossible to eradicate, hence the importance of keeping it out of Britain at all costs.

The following description of rabies is taken from the Final Report of the Committee of Inquiry on Rabies (CMND 4696), paragraph 4.23:

"In the dog, the first sign of rabies is usually a change of behaviour. The animal may seek seclusion in corners, or hide under furniture. Friendly dogs tend to become aggressive and make unprovoked attacks. The animal may howl in an unusual tone; fine muscular tremors may be accompanied or followed by paralysis in one or more limbs. There is often marked dilation of the pupils with a wild staring of the eyes. The animal may go off its food or, in attempting to eat, it may let food fall from its mouth. It may try to drink, but be unable to swallow. Excess salivation and frothing at the mouth may occur, and the animal may be constipated but still make great efforts to defecate. It may attack wooden or metal objects and cause serious damage to its teeth, mouth, claws and foot pads. If paralysis does not supervene, the animal may run long distances biting at anything in its path. Some animals suffer partial paralysis and run in circles with the head at an angle. As paralysis and twitching becomes progressively more marked, salivation decreases and, when finally exhausted, the animal usually lies on its side in convulsions. Gradually it becomes comatose and dies. When signs of great excitement predominate the disease is often called 'furious' rabies. In some animals, although many of the same signs occur, paralysis is predominant. The disease is then called 'dumb' rabies, and unless the animal is disturbed, the risk that it may bite is considerably less".

There is no cure, and immediately the disease is recognised the dog has to be destroyed.

Every precaution should be taken to prevent being bitten if rabies-like symptoms occur. In Great Britain it is a notifiable disease and all cases must be reported to the police. The dog must not be destroyed without authority and particularly not shot through the head, as the brain and spinal cord have to be available for laboratory examination by the Ministry of Agriculture.

Rheumatism—See Arthritis

Rickets

This condition is a malformation of the bones due to an imbalance of calcium and vitamin D in the body. Nowadays, thanks to better feeding of dogs, it is much less common, but it can still occur, particularly in larger, long-boned dogs, such as alsatians and great danes. The symptoms are poor bone growth, swollen joints, and at worst bones that bend, or fracture at a slight knock.

Prevention is achieved by giving a good balanced diet, and supplementing it with Sherley's Cod Liver Oil Capsules and Sherley's Calcium Tablets. Once symptoms have developed consult your veterinary surgeon. Considerable treatment may be needed to try to correct the situation.

Road Accidents—See Chapter 6

Skin Diseases—See Eczema and Chapter 5, External Parasites.

Slipped Disc

This is a popular term both in human and veterinary medicine, which is probably used also to describe many back-ache conditions. A true slipped disc is an acutely painful condition which usually results from the dog leaping or jumping unwisely. In many cases an X-ray may not show any obvious displacement of the vertebrae of the spine, but it seems that the spinal cord has been pinched.

Symptoms—The dog will often stand for hours, absolutely rigid, with the muscles standing out, especially around the neck area (cervical disc) in an attempt to avoid any painful movement. If forced to move it will often shriek out with pain. In less severe cases the dog will be heard to yelp, as it gets up, or may be unable to go up a step.

Treatment—In many cases rest, warmth, and pain-killing drugs will bring relief in a few days, but in severe cases an operation may be necessary. Sometimes paralysis will result (see Paralysis).

Scurf

This is a condition which seems to worry a great many owners. It is really just a shedding of the dry superficial scales of the skin. With a sensible balanced diet, plenty of exercise and regular grooming it should not be a problem. However, it is sometimes thought that both the perennial problem of shedding hair and scurf are probably aggravated by dogs living in over-warm centrally heated houses. If you are really worried by your pet's coat condition, always consult your veterinary surgeon.

Snake Bites—See Bites

Spaying

Spaying is the surgical sterilisation of female dogs—see Chapter 2.

Sprains

Sprains are caused by the overstretching of a muscle, or group of muscles. There is usually swelling, pain and in the case of a limb, lameness, but the condition can easily be confused with a fracture, or a local infection, so it is wiser to consult a veterinary surgeon.

Stings

Wasp and bee stings are very common in the summer months and cause considerable pain. If you are able to see the sting, lift it out carefully with tweezers and apply a pad of cotton wool wrung out in very cold water. In some cases the sting may produce an allergic reaction (see Allergy) and if the sting is in the mouth, as often happens, there may be considerable swelling of the tongue, salivation, and distress. Consult a veterinary surgeon, as antihistamine treatment will give quick relief.

Tail Injuries

Tails, because of their habit of wagging, seem rather prone to trouble. Some dogs develop a chronically bleeding tail (see Bleeding). Tails can also readily be sprained and even broken, from a knock and these seem to be very painful conditions. Some dogs are born with a kinked tail and while this is only a cosmetic fault, it may spoil them for showing.

Tail Docking—See Chapter 2 (Pups)

Tail docking is sometimes necessary in the older dog as a result of injury.

Teeth

Dogs, like people, have two sets of teeth, the temporary, or puppy teeth and permanent. The full set of second teeth are usually through by 6 months old. Regular care (see Chapter 4) will help your dog to keep his teeth, as will the avoidance of all sweet foods which help to cause decay. If extractions become necessary, face the facts, and realise that your dog will be much more comfortable and healthy without bad teeth. The gums harden, and many toothless dogs still enjoy gnawing at a bone.

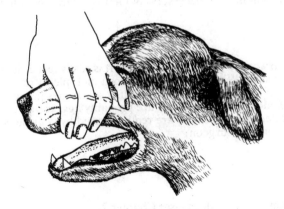

Examining a dog's teeth and mouth.

Teeth Abscesses—See Abscesses.

Distemper Teeth—These are teeth that have been damaged in their formative period by the fact that the pup has had some general disease (often distemper). When the second teeth come through, the enamel is seen to be pitted, and unfortunately nothing can be done to improve their appearance. The only consolation is that the teeth seem just as resistant to decay and last as long as normal teeth.

Third Eyelid—See Eye Conditions

Tonsillitis

The tonsils of the dog are oval, pinkish lymphatic glands situated at each side of the very back of the throat. In the normal dog they are very small and scarcely noticeable, but when infected they may be as large as hazelnuts in a large dog, and very red and inflamed.

Symptoms—Tonsillitis is most common in town dogs. There is difficulty in swallowing, loss of appetite, and the dog may run a temperature and feel quite ill.

Treatment—Consult a veterinary surgeon. Antibiotics give quick relief. Give soft and tempting foods to eat. Occasionally tonsillectomy (removal) is necessary.

Tumours

This term covers both malignant growths (cancers) and benign or harmless growths, and they may occur in any situation on or in the dog. As a general rule one can say that growths are usually painless in the early stages (unlike an abscess) and tend to grow comparatively slowly. The symptoms of internal tumours vary with their situation and they may be difficult to diagnose. Tumours in the uterus may be mistaken for pyometra symptoms or even pups, and tumours in the bladder may suggest bladder stones. If you suspect that your dog has a tumour do not delay in consulting a veterinary surgeon. An early operation is nearly always advised (unless the dog is very old or in poor health), and in the case of cancers this may be able to stop them forming secondary growths elsewhere.

Warts

Warts are really more of a nuisance than an illness, but they often have to be removed, because of the dog's unfortunate habit of biting or scratching at them, causing bleeding wounds.

Whelping—See Chapter 2

Wounds

Many people have the impression that dogs will lick wounds better, but in many cases they will actually make them much worse. As a rule wounds will heal more quickly when protected, both from germs and from the dog, and this is particularly the case in any surgical wound where there are stitches. Sherley's Veterinary Ointment is a valuable protection for small cuts and abrasions.

Chapter 8
SHERLEY'S AND AMPLEX DOG CARE PRODUCTS

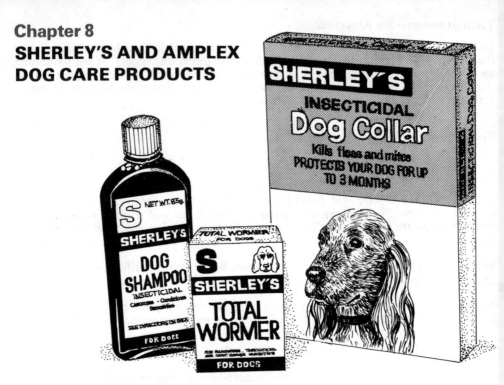

SHERLEY'S INTERNAL MEDICINES

Anti-Diarrhoea Tablets

Pleasantly flavoured tablets for the alleviation of symptoms in mild, uncomplicated cases of diarrhoea. Suitable for puppies and adult dogs.

Cold, Flu and Fever Tablets

A combination of analgesics to relieve pain and antipyretics to lower body temperature—the major symptoms of these conditions. Suitable for puppies and adult dogs.

Cough Linctus

Contains an anti-tussive to suppress the cough and a bronchodilator to relieve congestion of the lungs. Supplied in an easy-to-use dropper bottle and suitable for puppies and adult dogs.

Creo-Garlic Pills

Garlic is a traditional internal antiseptic, that can be of value in the treatment of infections, particularly those affecting the upper respiratory, bronchial and abdominal areas. For adult dogs only.

Gastrine Tablets

Formulated with antacids for the relief of indigestion, flatulence and other minor stomach disorders. Suitable for puppies and adult dogs.

Lik-A-Med Laxative

A gently-acting, savoury-flavoured lick-off cream laxative that is specially suitable for puppies. Given with a biscuit or placed on the nose, it is easy to administer and readily accepted.

Milk Suppression Tablets

Combined with a reduction in fluid intake, will reduce lactation. Valuable when puppies are removed from nursing mothers or in cases of false pregnancy when lactation occurs.

Rheumatine Tablets

A combination of anti-inflammatory and analgesic agents to relieve the symptoms of swelling and pain in muscular rheumatism and arthritis. For adult dogs only.

Sedative Tablets

An effective formula for calming highly-strung, nervous or excitable dogs. Particularly valuable during storms, fireworks or on other noisy occasions. For puppies and adult dogs.

Travel Sickness Tablets

Given before a journey, will soothe the system and help to prevent vomiting, to which dogs are very prone. Suitable for puppies and adult dogs.

SHERLEY'S EXTERNAL MEDICINES

Antiseptic Lotion

A safe formula topical antiseptic for the disinfection of wounds, bites, stings and abcesses. Can be used neat or diluted.

Canker Powder

Ideal for wet canker and otitis. Easily puffed into the ears, using the special pack, it heals, soothes and kills the mange and other parasites, that are a frequent cause of ear inflammations.

Canker Lotion Capsules

Particularly for dry canker and otitis, a warmed capsule is squeezed into the affected ear. Like the powder, it soothes and heals and is active against mange and other parasites.

Eczema & Mange Lotion

A soothing and healing non-greasy lotion particularly for wet conditions, containing calamine and an insecticide to control the mange mites and other parasites that commonly cause skin problems in dogs.

Eye Lotion Capsules

Sterile, antiseptic capsules for the treatment of inflamed, infective conditions of the eye. The tip of the capsule is removed and the lotion squeezed onto the eye.

Skin Cure

An oily preparation for dry cases of eczema and mange. Contains an insecticide to control the skin parasites that are usually associated with these conditions.

Veterinary Ointment

Has a firm anti-lick texture to prevent removal. For application to dry eczema, wounds, sores and burns, the ointment guards against infection, soothes and promotes healing.

AMPLEX DEODORANTS AND SHERLEY'S ACCESSORIES

Amplex Veterinary Tablets

The original Amplex Tablets in veterinary form. They help to control breath and body odours in dogs and can be effective in systemically overcoming the odour of bitches in season. For best results, use in conjunction with Amplexol liquid or No-Fol.

Amplexol

A concentrated deodorant and antiseptic liquid. Used diluted, it is ideal for cleaning and disinfecting dogs and especially effective in helping to mask externally the odour of bitches in season. Best used for this purpose with Amplex Veterinary Tablets. Can also be used as a disinfectant for materials and utensils around the house.

No-Fol

A pleasant-smelling but strong spray which applied to bitches in season has a masking and repellent effect. Should be used in conjunction with Amplex Veterinary Tablets.

Concentrated Disinfectant

Formulated especially for use in association with pets as well as generally in the house, it is not only germicidal and deodorant, but also contains an insecticide to eliminate parasites, such as fleas on baskets and bedding. Ideal for cleansing kennels, baskets and bedding and for general household purposes.

Repello

Aerosol spray to help prevent fouling by dogs. Sprayed onto places to be kept clean, such as gates, trees, shop-fronts and flower beds, the strong odour has a deterrent effect.

Savvy Stain Remover

A special stain remover for quickly cleaning and eliminating pet stains and smells from soft furnishings and upholstery. Helps to prevent damage, without leaving a tell-tale ring.

Spray Away

A harmless spray for regular use around the home to neutralise animal odours on furniture and furnishings, and to deodorise kennels, cages and baskets and bedding. Pay particular attention to corners and crevices.

Stop Chew

A safe but unpleasant-tasting liquid to spray onto articles to be protected from chewing. Discourages dogs and puppies from this destructive habit. Safe and can be used as often as necessary.

Swiftie

Has a special attractive odour, almost unnoticeable to humans. Used regularly on a newspaper or tray which is each time moved nearer the door, puppies are quickly and cleanly house trained. Helps prevent damaging accidents.

SHERLEY'S WORMING PREPARATIONS

Puppy Worming Syrup

Specially formulated for roundworm eradication in young puppies, in a convenient syrup presentation. Roundworm infestation, transmitted from the mother, frequently occurs in puppies and can be serious. Routine medication is advisable.

Worming Cream

The easy-to-use worming cream for roundworm in older puppies and adult dogs to which tablets are difficult to administer. It is pleasantly flavoured and placed on the nose, around the mouth or on a biscuit, will be readily licked off.

Roundworm Tablets

Liver-flavoured tablets specifically for roundworm. Ideal for routine treatment and prophylaxis in older animals.

Tapeworm Tablets

Specifically for tapeworm infestation, these tablets will eradicate the parasite in one day. Not for use in puppies under six months of age.

Total Wormer

A three week combination course of capsules that will deal with both roundworm and tapeworm at the same time. Ideal when the type of infestation is not known. Not for use in very young puppies.

SHERLEY'S INSECTICIDES AND PARASITICIDES

Insecticidal Dog Collar

This elegant, fabric secondary collar is impregnated with a powerful insecticide that kills fleas and mites for up to three months. Worn continuously, it prevents further re-infestation. Adjustable and available in two lengths, it will fit all sizes of dog. Not for use on puppies.

Flea-Free Medallion

A disc of insecticide in an unobtrusive plastic medallion that is attached to the normal collar. It will protect from fleas and other external parasites for up to two months.

Dog Band

A neat plastic secondary collar containing insecticide that is gradually released over three months to destroy fleas and ticks. Adjustable in length to fit any size of dog.

Vamoose Insecticidal Dog Powder

An extra strength insecticidal powder for use only on adult dogs. Rapidly destroys fleas, ticks, body lice and other parasites and used regularly, will prevent further attacks. Supplied in an easy-to-use puffer-pack. Can also be used on kennels, baskets and bedding.

Vamoose Insecticidal Pet Powder

A normal strength insecticidal powder for use on all household pets, including adult dogs, to control external parasites. Used like Dog Powder, it is not quite so rapid or lasting in effect.

Vamoose All-Purpose Insecticide

A convenient-to-use aerosol insecticide for use on adult and young dogs but not tiny puppies. Also suitable for many other animals and on bedding. Can be used generally around the home to destroy most common insect pests.

No Scratch

Scratching is usually the first sign of fleas. Used weekly, this powder will immediately eliminate them and protect from further infestation. Packed in handy puffer-pack.

Dog Shampoo—Insecticidal

As well as thoroughly cleaning and conditioning the coat, this shampoo destroys external parasites, particularly fleas and lice. Leaves the coat soft and healthy.

SHERLEY'S VITAMINS AND TONICS

Blood Salts

Contain balanced quantities of vitamins and minerals, including vitamin A, vitamin E, copper and manganese, essential to a dog's good health. A small quantity sprinkled on the food each day will prevent any deficiency of the active ingredients.

Calcium Tablets

With added vitamin D to assist intestinal absorption, this important mineral is essential to the formation of strong teeth and bones. Particularly valuable for young, pregnant or lactating animals.

Cod Liver Oil Capsules

A rich, natural source of vitamin A which helps to ensure a healthy coat, controls infection and maintains peak vision, and of vitamin D, which aids calcium absorption, thus ensuring proper teeth and bone development.

Energol B

A dietary supplement containing the ten factors of the important vitamin B complex, essential for proper functioning of the nervous system, the digestive system and the blood. Especially valuable for ensuring health, energy and vitality in older dogs.

Lintox Tonic

Phosphate-rich, this vitamin and mineral tonic helps aid recovery after illness, builds up resistance against further disease and given daily, helps to maintain good health.

Sherley-Vites Condition Tablets

Savoury-flavoured tablets containing a balanced combination of vitamins and minerals that all dogs need to maintain top condition. A daily dose will prevent any dietary lack of these substances and help to ensure peak health.

Wheat-Germ And Cod Liver Oil Tonic

Wheat-germ provides natural vitamin E, the vitality vitamin, and Cod Liver Oil provides vitamins A and D. All three are essential to good health and a valuable supplement to the normal diet.

SHERLEY'S FOODS

Lactol

Lactol is a milk food, scientifically formulated as a replacement or supplement for puppies and is also highly suitable for pregnant or nursing bitches as an addition to the diet. Cow's milk is not as rich as bitch's milk and is therefore not ideal for puppies. Lactol contains all the nutrients of natural bitch's milk in the correct proportions, plus added vitamins, in easily digestible form. (See table on page 34.)

Lactol Meal

An ideal first food for weaning puppies. Contains health-promoting liver-meal, bonemeal and malt. Can be served soaked in Lactol, water or gravy for very young animals, or dry when they become older.

Lactol Biscuits

Protein and Vitamin-rich biscuits, very suitable as an early solid food for young puppies. Can be given moist or dry.

Lactol Drops

Milky-white chocolate drops, ideal as a treat or tit-bit for your dog. High in food energy value, they contain a balanced selection of vitamins and can be used as a supplement to the normal diet.

Liver Snaps

Containing liver, wheat-germ and bonemeal phosphates, these highly nutritious biscuits make an ideal reward. For younger animals they should be crumbled and served moist.

Lactol Bones

A large, very hard bone-shaped biscuit. Safer, more hygienic than a real bone, it promotes dental health by exercising the teeth and is full of nutritious ingredients to aid good health.

SHERLEY'S AND AMPLEX GROOMING AIDS

Luxury Shampoos

A range of four luxury shampoos that cover every requirement for every type of dog:

Herbal Shampoo With Protein—Especially suitable for long-haired breeds, cleanses and conditions, helping to prevent brittleness and tangling.

Poodle Special Shampoo—Suitable for poodles of all colours. Enhances and beautifies the coat, highlighting the colour.

Coatacine Conditioning Shampoo With Balsam—Suitable for all breeds. Gives a long-lasting shine and silkiness to the coat.

Luxury Shampoo For Pedigree Breeds—A gentle shampoo for the softest coats, ideal for puppies and toy dogs as well. Delicate in action, providing the coat with a new lustre.

Dog Shampoo—Insecticidal

As well as thoroughly cleaning and conditioning the coat, this shampoo destroys external parasites, particularly fleas and lice. Leaves the coat soft and healthy.

Grooming Powder

An antiseptic powder that is rubbed into the coat, then brushed out. Cleans the hair and skin. Ideal for use in winter, when wet shampooing is often inconvenient.

Coatacine

A non-greasy, rapidly drying grooming tonic for the care of all breeds. Beautifies and imparts a rich glossy sheen to the hair. Used by breeders and exhibitors to add the final touch to an animal's appearance. Available as a liquid and in an easy-to-use aerosol pack.

Tear Stain Remover

Many breeds suffer from this unsightly problem. This is a safe, efficient and hygienic means of removing these stains. Used regularly it removes existing marks and prevents re-formation. Especially suitable for poodles.

Dry Bath

An elegant, lightly perfumed dry spirit shampoo that is rubbed into the coat for a healthy, fresh look. The hair does not become wet and it is particularly suitable for use in cold weather or on unwell animals.

Odour Cologne

A gentle perfume just for dogs. Keeps them fresh and sweet-smelling. It is a non-spirit compound of floral fragrances and a deodorant, supplied in an economical spray bottle.

Dry Clean

Specially processed flakes for cleansing and deodorising the coat. Very effective when the hair becomes greasy or badly soiled. Just rub in, then brush out.

Amplex Shampoos

Amplex Poodle Shampoo is specially formulated with almond oil for poodles. Produces a rich lather which beautifies and deodorises. **Amplex Deodorant Shampoo** cleanses, rinses easily and leaves the coat in healthy condition. **Amplex Spirit Shampoo** is a quick-to-use dry shampoo that is applied with a cloth. Massaged into the coat, it deodorises and beautifies.

Index

Index

Contents	Page No.	Contents	Page No.

Contents	Page No.	Contents	Page No.

Contents	Page No.	Contents	Page No.

New from Sherley's

SHERLEY'S
INSECTICIDAL
DOG BRUSH
Kills fleas, ticks & lice

The convenient, effective way to rid dogs of fleas, ticks and lice. Fast-acting Vamoose Insecticidal Dog Powder and a special de-luxe slicker brush are combined to keep your dog's coat clean and healthy throughout the year.

BRUSH IN—BRUSH OUT

You use the Sherley's Insecticidal Dog Brush just like an ordinary slicker brush (Fig 1). Carefully brush your dog all over, gently squeezing the Vamoose flask to give an even spread of powder throughout the coat.

DE-LUXE SLICKER BRUSH

Leave the powder on the coat for about 30 minutes to kill the parasites. Unscrew the Vamoose flask from the brushhead and screw in the separate handle (Fig 2). You now have a de-luxe slicker dog brush to groom out the powder.

REGULAR GROOMING

After grooming out the powder, remove the handle and wash the brush in warm soapy water. When reassembled with the handle, you can use the brush for your dog's regular grooming.

AVAILABLE JULY 1976